Foreword

At Young Writers our defining aim is to promote an enjoyment of reading and writing amongst children and young adults. By giving aspiring poets the opportunity to see their work in print, their love of the written word as well as confidence in their own abilities has the chance to blossom.

Our latest competition *Poetry Express* was designed to introduce primary school children to the wonders of creative expression. They were given free reign to write on any theme and in any style, thus encouraging them to use and explore a variety of different poetic forms.

We are proud to present the resulting collection of regional anthologies which are an excellent showcase of young writing talent. With such a diverse range of entries received, the selection process was difficult yet very rewarding.

From comical rhymes to poignant verses, there is plenty to entertain and inspire within these pages. We hope you agree that this collection bursting with imagination is one to treasure.

Contents

St Nicholas CW Primary School, Cardiff

Ysgol Cae Top, Bangor

The Poems

Love

Love is red like a heart full of gentleness.
It feels like a warm cosy hug.
It smells like roses at springtime.
It sounds like Cupid's arrows pinging.
It tastes like a Galaxy hot chocolate on a cold winter's day.
It reminds me of my family and that is love for me.

Zoe Gilchrist (10)
Alexandra Primary School, Airdrie

Gamble, The Fluffy Dog Diamantes

Gamble
Energetic mutt
Timid and shy
Small, loving and loud
Rushing, running, hurrying
Bright, noisy
Gamble

Gamble
Fluffy cloud
A fluff ball
Tiny, small little ball
Loud and fantastic
Cool, great
Gamble

Gamble
Loud bark
Shouts like mad
Howling like a wolf
Cries like crazy
Fluff ball
Gamble.

Ryan Gallagher (11)
Alexandra Primary School, Airdrie

Modern Warfare 2

M odern society
O wning people
D rowning in sea
E lectric magnetic pulse
R eally good
N ew map packs

W ar game
A cool game
R eally good
F antastic
A fter school
R apid fire
E xcellent

2 good for a game!

Daniel Chaudhry (12)
Alexandra Primary School, Airdrie

Fishing Tackle

F ish swimming in the water taking bait
I n the water fish fight for food
S plashing water where the waves hit land
H igh floats bobbing on the water
I n the tent you run when it starts to rain
N ot able to catch any more fish
G etting ready to have fish for dinner

T imid fish nibbling at worms and maggots
A ll different kinds of fish: trout, pike, perch
C arrying the fish home with pride
K illing fish when they are caught
L eaving the lake knowing you'll have a good dinner
E nthusiastic to do more fishing.

Matthew Robertson (11)
Alexandra Primary School, Airdrie

My Fat Cat

Cleo
You're fat
And you're fluffy
You're the best cat
White and ginger
And you're
Smart

Cleo
My cat
She's really nice
And she is fast
Mum and Dad
Love the
Cat.

Grant Stevenson (11)
Alexandra Primary School, Airdrie

Happiness

Happiness is yellow like the sun on a summer's day.
Happiness smells like fish and chips on a family trip.
Happiness sounds like water sloshing in a swimming pool in an exotic location.
Happiness tastes like ice cream on a sunny day.
Happiness looks like a five star hotel far, far away.
Happiness feels like sand running through your hand on a golden beach.
Happiness reminds me of my first holiday abroad.

Declan Donnelly (11)
Alexandra Primary School, Airdrie

Fun

Fun is yellow like the sun shining down on families at the park.
Fun tastes like chocolate.
Fun reminds me of going on holiday to the beach.
Fun sounds like laughter at a birthday party.
Fun looks like bubbles flying everywhere in the garden.
Fun feels like being cuddled up on the couch watching a movie.
Fun smells like popcorn at the cinema.

Rachel McKeown (10)
Alexandra Primary School, Airdrie

Love

Love is the colour red like a love heart.
It sounds like a bird's song early in the morning.
Love looks like a happy family playing on a beach.
It feels like soft silk running through your fingers.
Love tastes like freshly baked cookies on a winter's day.
Love smells like freshly cut flowers in the spring.
Love reminds me of a dozen red roses.

Lucy Gallagher (11)
Alexandra Primary School, Airdrie

Fun

Fun is green,
It smells of nature
And sounds like birds chirping.
Fun looks like a forest,
It feels like mud
And reminds me of a long walk in the woods.
Fun tastes of berries freshly picked of the trees.

Sophie Kane (10)
Alexandra Primary School, Airdrie

Fun

Fun is yellow like the warm hot sun.
Fun is full of laughter like sweaty, fun-loving kids.
Fun makes people have a great big smile on their face.
Fun makes children feel enjoyment inside themselves.
Fun makes everyone feel good.
Fun reminds me of long hot summer holidays playing football in the park.

Daniel Gallagher (10)
Alexandra Primary School, Airdrie

Sadness

Sadness is the colour of blue.
It sounds like someone crying.
It reminds you of when someone is dying.
It tastes of water.
It looks like a sad face
And feels like you are alone.

Simone Goodall (10)
Alexandra Primary School, Airdrie

Love

Love is white and smells like beautiful roses in the garden.
Love tastes of white chocolate melting in your mouth.
Love sounds like the loud music when my mum is in the car.
Love looks like a Valentine's card with lots of hearts on it.
Love reminds me of good times.

Jordan Offord (11)
Alexandra Primary School, Airdrie

Love

Love is red like joy and happiness,
All cosy and warm, in a heart.
Love also can be a box of chocolates,
Roses, kisses and children giving you hugs.

Nicole Keyes (10)
Alexandra Primary School, Airdrie

Potatoes

My mum had a bag of potatoes
And wondered what she could do.
Oh there's lots of things I could do with them
And here are just a few.

Firstly if you cut them thick,
You can make some lovely chips.
But when you cut them extra thin,
You can get lots of non-flavoured crisps.

If you keep the skin on,
There are lots of things to make.
Maybe some spicy wedges,
Or a jacket potato to bake.

Maybe you could mash it up
And add some milk and cream.
Then throw in some scallions,
Champ tastes just like a dream.

But waffles and smiley faces
Are my favourite type to eat.
But Mum rarely cooks them,
So when she does it's a lovely treat.

Aoife McGaughey (10)
All Saints Primary School, Omagh

Best Ways Of Eating Spuds!

Mum likes potato pie,
Without it she'd nearly cry.

Dad likes a lot of chips,
With lovely red sauce dips.

Aoife likes waffles and beans,
But she spills them over her jeans.

Aimee likes gravy and mash,
She eats it all in a dash.

The dog likes the whole lot,
Sometimes she eats a full pot.

But I just like crisps!

Ryan McGaughey (8)
All Saints Primary School, Omagh

The Wonders Of Pigs

My sister wanted a 'hot dog'
But she felt very sad,
Because when Mum opened the packet,
The sausages were all bad.

My brother wanted a bacon butty
But he was out of luck,
Because when Mum cooked the dinner,
She cooked a roast duck.

My sister wanted a pork chop
But things were not looking good,
Because when Mum went to the market,
The stalls had no nice food.

Chloe Campbell (11)
All Saints Primary School, Omagh

Apple

The farmer went into the orchard
to look at the apples on the tree.

Some were lying on the ground,
they were easy to see.

He picked up all the apples
that were lying loose

And brought them back into the house
to make some apple juice.

Alannah Sweeney (10)
All Saints Primary School, Omagh

Apple Man

Apple Man began in a tree,
Hanging up for us to see.

He began to get fat and round,
Until he fell to the ground.

The farmer put him into the sink,
He said, 'I'll go and get my wife, I think.'

She said, 'I'll go and make a start,
In baking a yummy apple tart!'

Peter Barrett (9)
All Saints Primary School, Omagh

Hedgehog

They hibernate in winter
A baby hedgehog is called a hoglet
A hedgehog is nocturnal
And is an insect eater.

Ryan Bainbridge (9)
Belvoir Park Primary School

Who Am I?

I am short and spiky,
I cat slugs and worms,
I live in a nest,
Owls like me for dinner,
I sleep all winter,
I like to sense and smell,
My baby is called a hoglet.
Who am I?

A hedgehog.

Kansas Burrows (8)
Belvoir Park Primary School

My Hamster Chunks

Hamsters can scratch.
Hamsters can be thin.
Hamsters are all sorts of colours.
Hamsters can hide.
Hamsters can sneak.
Hamsters can bite if they are scared.
Hamsters can climb.
Hamsters can make a plan.

Lauren Hylands (8)
Belvoir Park Primary School

What Am I?

I am brown and spiky,
I hibernate in winter,
I have a good sense of smell,
I hunt worms and slugs.

A hedgehog.

Max Phoenix (8)
Belvoir Park Primary School

Caterpillars Are . . .

Caterpillars are slow.
Caterpillars are red and green.
Caterpillars are camouflaged.
Caterpillars are colourful.
Caterpillars are hairless.
Caterpillars are tickly.
Caterpillars are smooth.
Caterpillars are short.

Ryan Gilchrist (8)
Belvoir Park Primary School

What Am I?

I eat worms, snails, frogs, beetles,
Yum-yum!
I hibernate in winter,
My eyesight is bad,
But my sense of smell is good.

Hedgehog.

Peter Savage (8)
Belvoir Park Primary School

Bees

Bees can fly.
Bees are quite small.
Bees can buzz.
Bees are black and yellow.
Bees make honey.
Bees are friendly and stripy too.

Rachel Sykes (8)
Belvoir Park Primary School

Teddy

Teddies are fun and peaceful.
Teddies are full of stuffing and love.
Teddies can be any colour.
They have big tummy patches.
They are soft, special, bumpy, cuddly and light.

Taylor Saunders (8)
Belvoir Park Primary School

Friends Are . . .

Friends are sharing a skipping rope
Friends are adventurous in the forest
Friends are fun playing chase
Friends are helpful.

Molly Craig (8)
Belvoir Park Primary School

Orange

Round, juicy
Nice, yummy
Scrummy fruit
Healthy, gorgeous.

Tegan McCullough (8)
Belvoir Park Primary School

The Blob

Green, stretchy
Blue and yellow
Sticky, small, squashy
Smelly, slimy and bouncy.

Hannah Martin (8)
Belvoir Park Primary School

Pee-The-Beds

I was walking down the street when I saw a bunch of pee-the-beds
so I went over to touch them.
After I touched them I ran all the way home
because it was eight o'clock
and ma mammy told me to be home at eight o'clock.
I went into ma house and ma mammy said,
'It's time for bed.'
'OK, night Mammy.'
'Night little one.'

One hour later
I woke up and I saw ma bed was wet
so I ran downstairs and shouted out, 'Mammy, Mammy.'
And ma mammy said, 'What is it?'
'I have peed the bed.'
'No you have not.'
'Yes I have.'
'No you have not, now sit down and watch the TV.'
'But Mammy can we go out later on?'
'Yes.'

Two hours later
'Mammy can we go out now?'
'Yes.'
We were walking down the street and I said to ma mammy,
'Mammy, look at that bunch of pee-the-beds, I am going to touch
them to see if pee-the-beds do make you pee the bed.'
'Well son, touch them all you like, pee-the-beds are not real.'
'Yes they are.'
We were walking home now.

Half an hour later
'We are home now, so go to bed son.'
'OK Mammy, but I am going to the toilet, OK?
I am out of the toilet now Mammy, night!'
'Night son.'

5 hours later
I heard footsteps coming upstairs and it was ma mamm
and she said to me, 'Are you still awake?'
'Yes.'
'Why?'
'Because I am waiting until I pee the bed.'
'Well you are not going to, because tonight you went to the toilet
before you went to bed, but last night you did not,
so that means pee-the-beds do not exist because you aren't going
to pee the bed so get to sleep and I will see you in the morning,
night.'
'Night, Mammy.'

Lisa Johnson (10)
Comely Park Primary School, Falkirk

My Beautiful Garden

There I sit at the bottom of the garden,
Surrounded by lots of colourful flowers.
Sunlight shining right down on me,
I could sit down here for hours and hours.

I can see the garden angels
Flying all around me.
Lovely butterflies fluttering by,
What a beautiful sight to see.

The chirping of birds,
And the buzzing of bees.
All through the garden,
Among the flowers and trees.

The garden is a wonderful place
To sit and think or dream.
It gives you peace and contentment,
My beautiful garden and me!

Kirsty Coleman (10)
Comely Park Primary School, Falkirk

...day
An... ...ut
Frown... ...ng glum
Bossing eve... ...ut.

Lunch times make ...s stomach turn
Custard, fish and mushy peas
'All school dinners stink,' he says
'Worse than rotten old blue cheese.'

But me, I think school's great
My teacher is so nice and sweet
She helps with problems and with work
For me sometimes my school's a treat.

At lunch I eat with all my friends
Food has vanished in a trice
We laugh and chatter as we eat
School dinners are extremely nice.

I'll really miss my primary school
When moving from one to another
I hope that things go well for me
Not like it is for my big brother.

Hannah Wilson (10)
Comely Park Primary School, Falkirk

Under The Sea

Under the sea there are lots of fish,
throw a coin in and make a wish.
There is seaweed and coral,
and a boat that is royal sails the sea on top.

One day I went diving,
it was worth trying to get the thrill that I did.
I dived right down, down, down, down,
until I thought I might drown.
So I pushed back up and that's when I saw it,
that's when I saw it, that tiny speck in the distance.

I was very curious so I was,
so I swam right up to that speck
and as I swam the speck got bigger
until it got bigger and I realised it was a shark.

I began to regret swimming up to that speck as I swam away,
for that speck was not so small anymore,
but the fish I feared the most.

Now sharks are very fast fish, far too fast for me!
So as I climbed up to my boat
the shark took a bite at my knee.

As I walked home on that unlucky day
I began t regret diving under the sea
because it left me with one leg.

Flora Smith (11)
Comely Park Primary School, Falkirk

Jake The Baker

Jake is a baker, he likes to eat cake
But where does he make cake?
It must be Jake the cake.

Harris Mackay (10)
Comely Park Primary School, Falkirk

School's Blown Up

The school has blown up
And I just got a new pup
    School's blown up
All the teachers are sad
But it is not bad
    School's blown up
Schools are not good
Because I am not in the mood
    School's blown up
All the boys and girls are happy
But babies need a nappy
    School's blown up
Blow, blow, blow, school, *boom!*
Blow, blow, blow, school, *boom!*
    School's blown up
Kaboom!

Louie Cattanach (10)
Comely Park Primary School, Falkirk

A Wish For A Fish

If ever I had a wish,
I'd wish for a blue fish.
I'd call him Bluebean,
His water would be clean.
He'd eat lots of food,
His eyes would show his mood.
His tank will be square,
He'll have Elvis hair.
He'll be a champion swimmer,
His scales will shimmer.
If ever I had a wish,
I'd wish for a blue fish.

Iona Roy (10)
Comely Park Primary School, Falkirk

The World

I went to Greenland,
it wasn't very green.

I went to the United States,
they weren't that united.

This world is a wonderful place,
but some names are a true disgrace.

I went to the Great Lakes,
they weren't too great.

I went to Hudson Bay,
but no one there was Hudson.

This world is a wonderful place,
but some names are a true disgrace.

Cameron Duff (10)
Comely Park Primary School, Falkirk

Winter!

When there is snow
When Christmas flows
When people are happy
The robins are flappy
So the birds fly south
And put pudding in your mouth
When the snowmen are built
And you go under your quilt
When leaves fall off the trees
And ice is on the seas
So you go to skate
With a big dinner on your plate . . .
It's winter.

Maisie McDavid (10)
Comely Park Primary School, Falkirk

My Mad Dad

Some people call him crazy land because he has a giant hand
He likes going to the gym but hates people singing hymns
He has three cats and is crazy for hats
He loves the Easter bunny, that means he's quite funny
When he has some food he is always in a good mood
If he sees a clown, he always makes a frown
He is afraid of heights and doesn't like bright lights
He has a favourite elf that sits on a golden shelf
Before he plays hockey he pretends to be a jockey
When he plays tennis he sings with his friend Denis
If you say my dad is who? This poem is my dad for you.

Ellie McAlpine (10)
Comely Park Primary School, Falkirk

Summer Love!

Summer is here and it is hot
Summer is here and I love it a lot
Go to the beach to get a tan
Go to the shops to buy a fan
Have a swim in the pool
Have a splash to keep you cool
Eat an ice cream
Eat all you can dream
Get your mum to buy you a toy
Get ready for the summer joy.

Caitlin Sinclair (11)
Comely Park Primary School, Falkirk

A Dessert Worth Rhyming For!

Tropical fruit from over the sea,
a yummy fruit salad all for me.

Mango, pineapple, papaya and blueberries,
all mixed together with just a few cherries.

Serve it with ice cream, cool and creamy,
makes a dessert delicious and dreamy.

Oh Mum, oh Mum, hear my plea,
make me a fruit salad for my tea.

Anna Steele (10)
Comely Park Primary School, Falkirk

Run

I hope one day I'll be free
to search the world for thee
the best person in the world
I'll hug him with my hair curled
as I hug him tightly and look over his shoulder
I see a very large boulder
the thing I spy with my eye
is the place where I will marry thee!

Aamarrah Hussain (10)
Comely Park Primary School, Falkirk

Egypt

E gypt, roasting and sandy
G old, precious and solid
Y oung ladies, pretty and happy
P haraoh, ruler and brave
T emple, famous and interesting.

Sophie Gilbert (7)
Comely Park Primary School, Falkirk

Football, The Game

Football, football is a brilliant game
It's always fun and never ever the same
With boots with studs and very long socks
When I touch the ball, my world rocks
We like to play on the grass
I'm always waiting for the pass
Then dribble past the defence like they're just little trolls
Then kick in the net, for lots of fantastic goals.

Jake Miller (10)
Comely Park Primary School, Falkirk

Yummy Worm!

I had a worm named Yummy
He died, he died
My mum told me he was sleeping
She lied, she lied
Why oh why is my worm dead?
Couldn't the postman run over me instead?

Morgan Lister (10)
Comely Park Primary School, Falkirk

My Little Brother

My little brother is a pest
but he still is the best.
My little brother likes to jump in puddles,
that's what gets him into trouble.
My little brother is like a bubble
because he gives me lots of cuddles.

Aisha Aamir (11)
Comely Park Primary School, Falkirk

Dearest Mum

To my dearest mum,
You've always been there
When I've hurt my thumb,
When I've broken a nail,
When I've hurt my bum.
I love you, my dearest mum.

Thomas Giffen (10)
Comely Park Primary School, Falkirk

Love

Love is pink like a glowing candle,
Love tastes like warm, bubbling chocolate cake,
Love smells like a sweet smelling rose,
Love looks like a garden of summer daisies,
Love sounds like an owl hooting in the twinkling stars,
Love feels like it will never end.

Toni Moore (10)
Comely Park Primary School, Falkirk

My Old Ragged Rug

My old ragged rug
It takes a bit of a tug
See my mucky pug
He made it . . .
My old ragged rug.

Sam McHale (10)
Comely Park Primary School, Falkirk

Love

Love is a love heart full of love.
Love feels like a warm cosy bed.
Love is as red as a rose.
Love smells like my mum and dad.
Love sounds like a heart beating.
Love tastes like sweets.
Love reminds me of my granny and grandad.

Hayley Bambrough (7)
Dunbar Primary School, Dunbar

Love

Love is a red heart
Love feels like being loved
Love is as red as a heart
Love smells like my beautiful mummy
Love sounds like my little sister when she is sleeping
Love tastes like Weetos
Love reminds me of my daddy.

Rhys Hainey (8)
Dunbar Primary School, Dunbar

Love

Love is as red as a beating heart.
Love feels like me cuddling my teddy bear.
Love is deep red.
Love smells of roses in a garden.
Love sounds like a stream in a wood.
Love tastes of pizza.
Love reminds me of my nan's dog Keira.

Eve Hexley (7)
Dunbar Primary School, Dunbar

Silence

Silence is as quiet as a slow tortoise.
Silence is as bored as a caterpillar.
Silence is black.
Silence smells like the sea.
Silence sounds like the beach.
Silence tastes of a juicy orange.
Silence reminds me of Glasgow.

Cameron Pike (7)
Dunbar Primary School, Dunbar

Sadness

Sadness is people crying.
Sadness feels like raindrops falling on my head.
Sadness is blue raindrops falling from the sky.
Sadness smells of raindrops.
Sadness sounds like thunder killing flowers.
Sadness tastes like water.
Sadness reminds me of my family.

Euan Ramage (7)
Dunbar Primary School, Dunbar

Love

Love is as red as roses.
Love feels like kisses.
Love smells like lavender.
Love sounds like a heart beating.
Love tastes like chocolate mice.
Love reminds me of my granny and grandad.

Mackenzie Lawler (7)
Dunbar Primary School, Dunbar

Surprise

Surprise is bright yellow like a daffodil
Just bursting with colour.
Surprise is luminous green
Like a leaping exotic frog.

Surprise smells like strawberries
Picked fresh from the garden.
Surprise smells like newly grown flowers
Smiling in the sunshine.

Surprise sounds like children in the sea
Jumping over the waves.
Surprise sounds like fireworks
Exploding in the sky on New Year's Eve.

Surprise tastes sweet like a toffee apple,
Crunchy on the outside and soft inside.
Surprise tastes like a pineapple,
Refreshing and cool.

Surprise looks like a Christmas tree
With lots of presents just for me.
Surprise looks like a jack-in-the-box
Waiting to pop out of his socks.

Surprise feels like a duck egg cracking,
Waiting to hatch and start quacking.
Surprise feels like a hot air balloon
Flying high in the sky in the afternoon.

Surprise reminds me of bubbles bursting
When I'm in the bath.
Surprise reminds me of Christmas Day
When I've opened my presents and Santa's gone away.

Scott Watson (10)
Edenderry Primary School, Portadown

Wonder

Wonder is white like Sleeping Beauty's dress,
Wonder is green meadow grass,
Wonder is silver like stars in the sky at night.

Wonder smells like an excited boy opening a surprise,
Wonder smells like a princess skipping through bright fields,
Wonder smells like an open cave waiting to be discovered.

Wonder sounds like a raging river with thousands of fish below,
Wonder sounds like a quiet library with minds thinking hard,
Wonder sounds like explorers in an old castle.

It tastes like thousands of fish waiting to be eaten,
It tastes like sour cream and cheese Pringles with a pinch of chilli,
It tastes like mashed potatoes being eaten with the Queen.

Wonder looks like stunt planes flying through waves and over
houses,
Wonder looks like a giant shop with thousands of people,
Wonder looks like a big field with rabbits playing with mice.

Wonder feels like another life inside you making you go to exciting
places,
Wonder makes your mind awaken and gives you a jump-start,
It takes control of you, sending your mind a tingle of wonder.

Wonder reminds me of people surfing, doing tricks and getting wet,
It reminds me of sports day when people run as quick as cars,
Wonder reminds me of scoring three goals in my first ever football
match.

Bryce McDowell (10)
Edenderry Primary School, Portadown

Confused

I am . . . well I'm not sure
No wait, it's definitely   *C*
Yes, that's it . . .
Or is it?

No, now I'm sure it's   *O*
Yes, that's . . . erm
I think it's probably   *N*

Why do I keep getting . . .
What's that word?
I am guessing
It begins with . . .   *F*

Right, I'll just skip to the next one
'What is the last vowel in this sequence?
A, E, I, O . . . '
I know this one, it's   *U*

Or no!
That's not it but I don't know what the answer is
So I'll just have to take a random guess
This one! No I pick   *S*

This is really hard
I'm only on question   *E*
And I don't want to get my results
It'll probably be a   *D*

I really do think I'm getting a bit . . . confused!

Alana Doyle (11)
Edenderry Primary School, Portadown

Excited

The morning had arrived
My tummy had some butterflies
I could hardly get my breakfast down
My tummy made a rumbling sound
I felt so excited

As I was in the car my knees were wobbling
I wanted to jump up and down
And run around
I was so excited

As we got there
I wanted to shout out loud
And deafen the crowd
That had gathered around

I was so excited
That everyone was talking around me
But I could not hear a thing
All I wanted to do was get on the pitch and win
I was so excited

Playing in a cup final
Is the most exciting feeling you can have
Especially when you win and go up to lift the cup
I was so excited.

Daniel Robb (11)
Edenderry Primary School, Portadown

Joy

Joy is yellow like the dazzling bright sun,
Joy is red like strawberry ice cream on a hot day,
Joy is pink like the wrapping on your birthday present.

Joy smells of red roses,
Joy smells of perfume that wafts through your senses,
Joy smells of dark chocolate sweets.

Joy sounds of birds singing through the day,
Joy sounds of the ice cream van as it drives down the road,
Joy sounds of children laughing as they play.

Joy tastes of magic fizzy elves,
Joy tastes of southern fried chicken noodles as a Friday treat,
Joy tastes of Coca Cola bubbles bursting on your tongue.

Joy looks like a meadow of flowers,
Joy looks like one million dancing medals,
Joy looks like laughing people having fun.

Joy feels like flying above all the clouds,
Joy feels like playing with your friends,
Joy feels like someone giving you a surprise.

Joy reminds me of flowers,
Joy reminds me of making new friends,
Joy reminds me of being encouraging.

Hannah Knowles (10)
Edenderry Primary School, Portadown

Fear

Fear is black
Like a huge, dark, creepy cave
That makes spooky noises.

Fear smells like rotted potatoes
Squelching through your fingers
Fear smells like ice
Trembling down your spine.

Fear sounds like cats
Squealing through the night
Fear sounds like heavy footsteps
Following everywhere you go.

Fear tastes like spicy curry
Making you sweat inside and out.

Fear looks like a gang of bullies
Waiting to pounce.

Fear feels like a cold shiver
Rattling through your bones
Fear feels like a bull
Charging fiercefully towards you.

Fear reminds me of the night
Dark, spooky and full of creepy noises.

Rhys Coulter (10)
Edenderry Primary School, Portadown

Excitement

Excitement is gold like a bright sun,
Excitement is silver like a sparkling ring,
Excitement is yellow like the soft smooth sand.

Excitement smells like the salty sea,
Excitement smells of a big bundle of candy,
Excitement smells of freshly cut grass.

Excitement sounds like happy kids laughing,
It sounds like cheering at a hockey match,
Excitement sounds like an orchestra.

Excitement tastes like sparkling lemonade,
Excitement tastes like melting ice cream,
Excitement tastes like popping candy.

Excitement looks like a bird learning to fly,
Excitement looks like fireworks,
Excitement looks like a shooting star.

Excitement feels like a whole bunch of butterflies in my tummy,
Excitement feels like sliding down a helter skelter,
Excitement feels like a helicopter ride.

Excitement reminds me of Christmas Eve,
Excitement reminds me of a hot summer's day,
Excitement reminds me of my birthday.

Lauren Shirley (10)
Edenderry Primary School, Portadown

Loneliness

Loneliness is grey like your room in the middle of the night
And black like a starless sky.
Loneliness is dark blue like being at the bottom of the sea.

Loneliness smells of moulded cookies and bread
And smells like a sewer full of rats.
Loneliness smells like rotted animal bones.

Loneliness sounds of silence
And people making fun of you.
Loneliness sounds like ghostly noises in your room at night.

Loneliness tastes like bitter raspberries and strawberries
And tastes like stale biscuits.
Loneliness tastes of food that shouldn't be mixed.

Loneliness looks like a dull and gloomy day
And looks like someone who is very depressed.
Loneliness looks like a farmyard with no animals in it.

Loneliness feels painful and isolated
And feels lonesome and forsaken.
Loneliness feels overwhelming and unsure.

Loneliness reminds me of being abandoned
And separated from your family and friends.
Loneliness reminds me of being left behind.

Sarah Hamilton (10)
Edenderry Primary School, Portadown

Love

Love is the colour red like a heart glowing bright,
Love is the colour blue, her eyes say it all to me,
Love is the colour yellow, the sun that shines on me.

Love smells of cherries, cherries on a cake,
Love smells of roses just freshly picked,
Love smells of chocolate, chocolate being poured.

Love sounds like laughter when dancing at a party,
Love sounds like music, it fills you up with joy,
Love sounds like birds singing in the sky.

Love tastes of chocolate melting in my mouth,
Love tastes of pie being pulled from an oven,
Love tastes of strawberries glowing bright red.

Love looks like flowers with a nice sense of smell,
Love looks like candy, as big as your red lips,
Love looks like you when you smile to say hello.

Love feels like wool, white and keeps you warm,
Love feels like sunshine, bright and keeps you smiling,
Love feels like grass, growing and keeps us cheerful.

Love reminds me of your face when I wake up and say hi!

Brett Smyth (10)
Edenderry Primary School, Portadown

Joy

Joy looks like the colours of the rainbow in the sky,
Joy makes me feel as if I can fly,
Joy smells like flowers and sounds like tweeting birds,
Joy tastes like sparkling lemonade that pops in my mouth,
And reminds me of sunshine shining down on my house.

Ross McMorris (10)
Edenderry Primary School, Portadown

Excitement Poem

Excitement is bright yellow like the sun on a summer's day.
Excitement is deep red like a sports car on a race track.
Excitement is white like the surf of big waves.

Excitement smells like a rich chicken curry on a cold night.
Excitement smells like a chocolate factory.
Excitement smells like my mum cooking my favourite meal.

Excitement sounds like water rushing over a giant waterfall.
Excitement sounds like the crowd cheering a goal at the World Cup final.
Excitement sounds like people waiting to go on holiday.

Excitement tastes like icing on a birthday cake.
Excitement tastes like popping candy.
Excitement tastes like a cool glass of orange juice in the sun.

Excitement feels like the smooth wrapping paper on a present.
Excitement feels like the warm sun on my face.
Excitement feels like a big hug from someone you love.

Excitement reminds me of playing in Spain.
Excitement reminds me of running on sports day.
Excitement reminds me of scoring a goal in a football match.

Ryan Upton (9)
Edenderry Primary School, Portadown

Emotions

I always wanted more from you
than you were willing to give,
so now we've gone our separate ways
each with different lives to live.
The bond will always be there,
the friendship always intact,
but the time for us has come and gone
and the pages of time, you can't turn back.
I will always be a friend to you
and I'll wonder how you are,
the smiles and laughter I will remember
and our fights have become painless scars.
Sometimes on those busy days
when you've a thousand things to do,
please let me glide slowly through your mind
and spend some time with you.
In a quiet moment when you're surprised to find me there;
just remember even with the distance between us,
I am still someone who cares.

Jay Cannaway (11)
Edenderry Primary School, Portadown

Hunger

Hunger is green like Nessie the Loch Ness monster.
Hunger is red like raw meat frozen not cooked.
Hunger is orange like a plump orange.
Hunger smells like the aroma of KFC splashing in your face.
Hunger sounds like a waiter taking your order.
Hunger tastes like bitter sour lemons.
Hunger looks like a barren empty desert with no life at all.
Hunger feels like squishy stuff.
Hunger reminds me of tasteless food.

Jonathan McKinley (10)
Edenderry Primary School, Portadown

Fear!

Don't move,
Not a move,
Not even one,
Don't make any movement.

Do you hear?
What's that noise
Going in and out
Like a creaking door?

Smell, what is it?
It smells like the sewers,
It makes you gag
And your stomach churn.

It looks like a black ball
Following you,
It's like a cut that won't heal,
It's like the shadow you don't want.

It's fear!

Chelsea Cinnamon (11)
Edenderry Primary School, Portadown

Confused

I am going to eat a snack
No, I'm going to . . .
Erm, I'm going to get my breakfast!
Hold on, it's lunchtime
No, it can't be lunchtime
It's dark but I'm in school
Urgh, I'm so shocked
I mean so confused!

Lauren Uprichard (11)
Edenderry Primary School, Portadown

Sadness

Sadness is pitch-black like people at a funeral
and like being alone in a tunnel.

Sadness smells like a dying rose
that is black and greyish,
you would be sneezing out of your nose.

Sadness sounds like people crying at a funeral,
they can't stop but they are trying.

Sadness tastes like an old pear,
the only thing that people do if they are sad is glare.

It looks like a sad little girl in her room crying,
won't stop crying but she is trying.

It feels like your stomach rumbling,
your eyes tearing up and your hands sweating.

It reminds me of a little girl in trouble
and crying in her room.
She is grounded and trying to stop soon.

Frances Nicole Kinazo Camello (10)
Edenderry Primary School, Portadown

Fear

Fear is very small,
The size of a pin,
It is so small you usually can't see it.

It hides behind you,
It hides inside you
And still you can't see it.

Until,

You look for it,
And you find it,
And then you can see it.

Once you find it,
It will *grow,*
And *grow,*

It will never go away again,
It might shrink but
It will always be there, at the back of your mind.

Bethany Proctor (11)
Edenderry Primary School, Portadown

Happiness

Happiness is blue like Chelsea fans cheering when they won the Premier League.
Happiness is yellow like the sun beating down on a summer's day.
Happiness smells like fresh flowers growing in the flower field's flower beds.
Happiness smells like the sea when you're on a luxury cruise with family.
Happiness sounds like children splashing at the seaside on a summer's day.
Happiness sounds like birds tweeting in the trees.
Happiness tastes like strawberry ice cream on a hot day.
Happiness looks like children playing outside in the sun at the park.
Happiness looks like flowers growing in the field.
Happiness feels like playing on the Xbox.
Happiness reminds me of going to my caravan and playing football and water fights.
Happiness reminds me of having a picnic in the park.

Gordon Cinnamon (10)
Edenderry Primary School, Portadown

Fear

Fear is like a thing that you can't fight or win.
Fear is like a black smoke.
Fear is like when you go to the doctor's and hear the patients scream for help.
Fear is when a dentist makes his drill scream.
Fear is when you are confined in a small room
with nowhere to go and no one to hear you.
Fear is in everyone.
Fear is in the mind.
That is what fear is . . .
What is your fear?

Fabien Durand (10)
Edenderry Primary School, Portadown

Confused

What should my poem be?
Oh what should it be?
Should it be six lines,
Or should it be three?
Maybe fourteen,
Or maybe ten?

Should it be about love,
Or should it be about hate?
Possibly jealousy,
Or I might do happiness?

What will I do for my poem?
I am not sure.
I don't know.
I can't make up my mind.
It's like a sour taste that never goes away.
I'm confused!

Thomas James McBroom (11)
Edenderry Primary School, Portadown

Happy!

Happy is fun, happy is excitable,
Happy is chocolate and ice cream,
Happy is playing with all my best friends.
Why can't we all be happy?
Happy is multicoloured,
Happy is a gift.
Why can't we all be happy?
Happy is a swirl of pink candyfloss,
Happy is the sun and moon smiling at me,
Happy is a swan gracefully swimming.
Why can't we all be happy?

Rebekah Forde (11)
Edenderry Primary School, Portadown

Random

I feel happy,
Now I feel sad,
No, now I feel jolly,
No, I am one hundred per cent sure that I feel crazy.

Maybe I feel anti-social,
But at the same time amicable!

I like sheep,
I like roof tiles,
I like tables
And even Aesop's fables!

I envy the bids,
They fly in the sky,
I envy the butterflies,
Fluttering by.

Today I think I am feeling random.

Jack Fletcher (11)
Edenderry Primary School, Portadown

Rage

I stand up tall looking down,
With my hands clenched up,
My eyes looking down,
At all the things that look like ants,
I feel like crushing them,
But I will be all alone,
Even though I want to get my own back.
I feel like pounding everybody in my path,
As for what people did to me,
One day in sorrow and pain,
Then next in rage and anger.

Alastair Henry (10)
Edenderry Primary School, Portadown

Being Nervous

Nervous is when you get butterflies in your stomach,
When you have wobbly knees from head to toe.

It can be a bitter taste,
It sounds like the after shocks of an earthquake,
People shouting as loud as they can,
Unsure what's going to happen next.

You might have heavy breathing,
Mixed emotions and nail biting, all at once.

Nervous can be exciting,
With all the different feelings,
Like panic, fear and fretting,
But it's good to be nervous sometimes,
Because it lets you feel all these emotions at once.

Nikita Murphy (10)
Edenderry Primary School, Portadown

The Dreamer

I'm lying in a field looking at the sky,
Someone comes over to me, they say, 'Hi.'
I say, 'Go away, I'm trying to sleep.'
He walked away and began to weep.
I looked at the beautiful clouds,
They spelt a word, it said lackadaisical.
I'm not lackadaisical!
The person weeping said, 'You're in denial.'
I just gave him a sarcastic smile.
I walked away and began to weep,
Then I fell asleep,
Suddenly I woke up,
It was all a dream,
I was confused.

Peter McKeeman (11)
Edenderry Primary School, Portadown

Fear

Fear is a thing
That is sharp
Like a knife.

Fear is a thing
That is sharp
Then smooth.

Fear is red and hot
Like a chilli sauce
That burns your tongue
Like mad.

Fear makes your body
Jump like a jack-in-the-box.

Claire Crowe (11)
Edenderry Primary School, Portadown

Fear

Fear is a pitch-black that whispers in your ear.
Fear is a blank thought of your mind.
Fear is a shadow that hovers over you.

Fear hides until midnight,
Then it looks at you.
It crawls into your mind
And takes control of you.

Fear can take over you
But remember this,
It can only take over you,
If you let it in.

Katie Elliott (11)
Edenderry Primary School, Portadown

Winter Days

Winter days,
bring the falling snow.
Spring days,
bring baby lambs playing happily in their fields.
Summer days,
bring the hot, hot sun and everyone out to play.
Autumn days,
bring howling wind that rustles the leaves.

Seasons are wonderful,
they bring the cold, heat, snow and sun,
they bring the fun.

Winter days,
bring the cold and Christmas.
Spring days,
bring the flowers and seedlings.
Summer days,
bring ice cream and lollies.
Autumn days,
bring Halloween and trick or treaters.

Winter days,
spring days,
summer days,
autumn days
    are fun!

Molly Newman (8)
Fairfield Primary School, Penarth

Wonders Of The World

The world is full of amazing places,
different people, different faces.

From the colossal Coliseum,
to the Natural History Museum.

The world is full of amazing places,
different people, different faces.

From the extraordinary Eiffel Tower,
to the Statue of Liberty and all of its power.

The world is full of amazing places,
different people, different faces.

From the Taj Mahal and its spires of gold,
to stupendous Stonehenge standing old and bold.

All this history and all this mystery
is for our pleasure and for us to treasure.

Benjamin Evans (10)
Fairfield Primary School, Penarth

Love

Love is like Heaven, up above the clouds
in the beautiful blue sky.
It sounds like the heart pounding.
Love tastes bitter and sweet.
Love is red.
Love looks like lips.
It feels romantic.
Love is romance!

Rebecca Wright (9)
Fairfield Primary School, Penarth

Happiness For Me And You

To me happiness is friendship,
but to you it could be fun.
Playing with your friends
or lying in the sun.

Happiness means everything
to me and to you,
whatever you do happiness is
for me and for you.

Remember now, think happy
and what happens to me and you.
Great things will come eventually
for me and for you.

Lauren Stephens (10)
Fairfield Primary School, Penarth

Guess What?

Sharp yellow teeth
Outgrown toes
Horrible nails
A pointy nose
A scary look
A piercing stare
A grunt and a groan
A frightening glare
Evil eyes
Pulsating hives
Argh! It's a goblin
Run for your lives!

Jade Eastwood (10)
Fairfield Primary School, Penarth

The Storm

The blackening darkness surrounds me,
The teasing hail crashes against my skin,
This frightens me.
The howling wind blows me away into the distance.
Will I ever get home?
The rain covers my tears.
Sun, please beam through the darkness
And assist me on my way.

Emily Button (9)
Fairfield Primary School, Penarth

Fairies In The Woods

The woods, the woods,
Oh how I love the lovely woods,
The pretty fairies in the trees,
Hiding behind rustling big green leaves,
Jumping from branch to branch,
Making such a beautiful dance,
How wonderful to see.

Hannah Salmon (9)
Fairfield Primary School, Penarth

Joy

Joy smells like steak, burgers and ketchup
Joy tastes like pizza and mouth-watering sweets
Joy sounds like laughter and talking
Joy looks like people playing
Joy is as peach as my friends
Joy feels like winning a massive trophy
Joy reminds me of my best friends.

Jack McKenna (9)
Hallside Primary School, Cambuslang

A Classroom Recipe

With a sprinkle of some rudeness
And a blob of noisiness
That is how you make your teacher angry

Add in some naughtiness
With a dash of shouting
That is how you make your teacher angry

But if you add a bowl full of kindness
And if you mix in some hard work
That is how you make your teacher happy

So add a teaspoon of smartness
And add a squirt of listening
That is how we make our teacher happy.

Iqra Tariq (9)
Hallside Primary School, Cambuslang

A Classroom Recipe

A pot of interruptions
A bowl of bad manners
That is how you make our teacher angry

A blob of nastiness
A sprinkle of noisiness
That is how you make your teacher angry

A scoop of happy faces
A dollop of good behavior
That is how you make your teacher happy

A hint of good homework
A handful of neat work
That is how we make our teacher happy.

Amy Morton (9)
Hallside Primary School, Cambuslang

A Classroom Recipe

With a dollop of bad manners
And a dash of interruptions
That is how you make your teacher angry

With a sprinkle of unfinished work
Mix in some noisy talking
That is how you make your teacher angry

But if you squirt in some hard work
And chop in some good listening
That is how you make your teacher happy

So add a hint of politeness
And shake in some good spelling
That is how we make our teacher happy.

Brooke Fernie (9)
Hallside Primary School, Cambuslang

A Classroom Recipe

With a sprinkle of interruptions
And a dollop of shouting out
That is how you make your teacher angry

Mix in some talking in class
And a squirt of bad manners
That is how you make your teacher angry

But if you add in some kindness
And chop in some good listening
That is how you make a teacher happy

So chop in some good manners
And add in some hard work
That is how we make our teacher happy.

Amber Kennedy (9)
Hallside Primary School, Cambuslang

A Classroom Recipe

If you sprinkle a touch of bad homework
And mix in some unfinished work
That is how you make your teacher angry.

If you add a blob of anger
And shake in some talking
That is how you make your teacher angry.

If you add in some politeness
And a chop of kindness
That is how you make your teacher happy.

If you squirt in some listening
And add a touch of hard work
That is how you make our teacher happy.

Cameron Fulton (9)
Hallside Primary School, Cambuslang

A Classroom Recipe

With a teaspoon of shouting out .
With a splat of bad manners
That's how you make your teacher angry

With a dollop of bad words
Then chop in some bad listening
That's how you make your teacher angry

With a squirt of hard work
Then a pinch of good behavior
That's how you make our teacher happy

So scoop in a bit of politeness
Then mix in a bit of kindness
That's how we make our teacher happy.

David Thompson (9)
Hallside Primary School, Cambuslang

A Classroom Recipe

A squirt of not listening
And a blob of shouting out
That is how you make your teacher angry

And if you add a hint of bad behavior
With a shake of unfinished work
That's how you make your teacher angry

But if you tap in some good homework
And mix in a dollop of good listening
That's how you make your teacher happy

So chop in some happiness
And dash in some concentrating
That's how you make our teacher happy.

Andrew Lindsay (9)
Hallside Primary School, Cambuslang

A Classroom Recipe

With a dash of carry on
And a scoop of bad manners
That is how you make your teacher angry

Add in a dollop of laughter
And a hint of silliness
That is how you make your teacher angry

But if you chop in some good listening
And if you blob in some helping out
That is how you make your teacher happy

So shake in some hard work
And add a bit of kindness
That is how we make our teacher happy.

Lucy Rosenbloom (9)
Hallside Primary School, Cambuslang

A Classroom Recipe

With a dash of shouting out
And a hint of bad manners
That is how you make your teacher angry

Add some bad behavior
And a squirt of graffiti
That is how you make your teacher angry

But if you mix in some hard work
And add a sprinkle of good listening
That is how you make a teacher happy

With a blob of brilliant behavior
And a scoop of kindness
That is how we make our teacher happy.

Caitlin Spiers (9)
Hallside Primary School, Cambuslang

A Classroom Recipe

With a pocketful of unfinished homework
And a pinch of bad concentration
That is what makes your teacher angry

With a mouthful of bad manners
And a blob of bad behavior
That is how you make your teacher angry

But if you take a spoonful of finished work
And shake some good eye contact
That is how you make your teacher happy

So mix in some good listening skills
And squirt in some kindness
That is how we make our teacher happy.

Hannah Paterson (10)
Hallside Primary School, Cambuslang

My Dad And Mum

My dad is a Ferrari
A lovely yellow daffodil in a meadow
Vibrant orange in a grey field
And that's my dad.

My mum is a pink flower in the darkest sea
A Lamborghini
Lively yellow in the rainbow
And that's my mum.

John Rowan (10)
Hallside Primary School, Cambuslang

Silence

Silence tastes like chocolate cake on a hot summer's day.
It's as sweet as ice cream on a cold winter's day.
Silence looks like a new baby coming into the Earth.
Silence smells like a rose growing and growing.
Silence is cream, it is red, it is yellow and blue.
Silence feels like a dream, it feels like Heaven.
Silence sounds like peace and quiet.
Silence reminds me of when I'm reading a book.

Eilidh McEwan (8)
Hallside Primary School, Cambuslang

Love

Love sounds like birds tweeting, wind blowing and people singing.
It smells of lovely flowers, smoky barbecues and animals.
Love tastes like hot dogs, sandwiches and jelly.
It feels like hot, warm and dry weather.
The colours of love are ink, yellow and purple.
Love looks like the beach, a holiday and a paddling pool.

Ross Elder (8)
Hallside Primary School, Cambuslang

Love

The colour of love can be red, pink or yellow
Love smells like roses, daisies and daffodils
Love sounds like tweeting birds in the sky
Love feels like you are flying in the air
Love tastes like happiness
Love looks like a big love heart in the sky
It reminds me of a fancy restaurant and champagne.

Antonia Kenna (9)
Hallside Primary School, Cambuslang

Sadness

Sadness sounds like a wee boy crying.
Sadness tastes like the water from the tears.
Sadness feels damp, soggy and wet.
Sadness looks like unhappy faces.
Sadness feels like a bullet in your back.
Sadness - the colours are grey and black.

Adam Patton (9)
Hallside Primary School, Cambuslang

Excitement

Excitement feels like happiness and fun
It is blue, red and yellow
It looks like roses and faces
It sounds like people laughing and talking
It smells of flowers and happiness
It tastes like hot sausages.

Ewan Little (9)
Hallside Primary School, Cambuslang

Happiness

It feels like glorious moments like Heaven.
It tastes like a glass of wine on a summer's day.
It is the colour of burgundy.
It looks like summer days in a fancy hotel.
It smells of a rose.
It reminds me of a holiday in Orlando.

Blair Sutherland (9)
Hallside Primary School, Cambuslang

Summer Days

Bright summer days that feel like hot days on the beach.
Just sitting looking at all the lovely colours; red, green, blue and yellow.
Just smelling the gentle breeze and the rose petals.
It feels like just sitting down, having a glass of rose wine.
It reminds me of sitting in a very rich country.

Dean Rodgers (9)
Hallside Primary School, Cambuslang

Nature

I see the squirrels climbing the trees.
I smell the beautiful roses in the grass.
I hear the squirrels chewing on the nuts.
I taste the sweet strawberries.
I feel the sun heating me up in the fresh air.

Callum Fergus (10)
Hallside Primary School, Cambuslang

Nature

I see the insects rushing in the green grass.
I hear the spiders walking on the wet ground.
I smell the salt seawater.
I taste the freshly picked strawberries and all of the other veg.
I feel the hot weather wrapping around me.

Lauren McAllister (9)
Hallside Primary School, Cambuslang

Nature

I see the bumblebees go to the flowers.
I hear the birds singing in the morning.
I smell the beautiful rose's pollen in the flower bed.
I taste the crunchy fresh apples from the tree.
I feel the beautiful breeze in the air.

Lewis Cameron (9)
Hallside Primary School, Cambuslang

Nature

I see the beautiful butterflies landing on the bright yellow daisy
I hear the waves crashing around in the sea
I smell the lovely air that wraps around me
I taste the honey after it's made by the busy, buzzing bees
I feel the smooth grass as it shivers.

Jessica Anderson (9)
Hallside Primary School, Cambuslang

A Spring Evening

I smell the lovely flowers gently swaying in the wind.
I see the bright sun shining in the sky.
I feel the sweat running down my neck.
I hear the song birds singing from their nests.
I taste the lovely ice-cold water.

Emily Reynolds (10)
Hallside Primary School, Cambuslang

The Orchestra Of The Sea

The sea is like an orchestra where birds sing in tune
Like a high-pitched flute or wood chime
And sand crunches like cracking maracas.

Seagulls glide across the big blue sky
And sound like soft violins
And pebbles make a snap as they crash to the ground
And bang like a big bass drum.

Waves gracefully float as they smash against the rock
And sound like noisy rain sticks or cymbals
And ships rattle like a big drowsy tuba.

Under the deep blue sea fish wiggle
And sound like guitars making a beat
And shells get carried away by the ocean's current
And silently ting like a triangle.

Sharks pounce like an electric guitar being vicious
And seaweed waves quietly like a fluttery harp.

The sea is like an orchestra
And it makes me want to be there all of the time.

Reece Ferguson (11)
Kelty Primary School, Kelty

The Orchestra Of The Sea

The clear, reflecting sea is like a beautiful, dancing orchestra,
Where slimy, smelly seaweed lies on the rocks like a calm, gentle harp
And crashing, smashing waves hit against the rocks like a booming bass drum.

An old, battered shipwreck is tossed around
Like a loud, crashing cymbal,
While the ship's old horn hoots like a screeching, groaning oboe,
Meanwhile scared people scream on the sandy seashore
Like a loud tooting trumpet.

Beneath the magical blue sea,
A gorgeous, cheerful mermaid glides along gracefully,
Like a slow, calm violin,
A tiny, curvy sea horse bounces along merrily,
Like a jumpy, happy flute.

Beware of the spiky, scary pufferfish
That lurk in the deepest, darkest waters,
Like a small, squeaky triangle,
Waiting to strike its prey
As a group of pinching, orange crabs wait to snap something up for dinner,
Like clicking, snapping castanets.
The orchestra of the sea gathers.

Catriona McInally (10)
Kelty Primary School, Kelty

The Orchestra Of The Sea

The beautiful shiny sea is like a dancing magnificent orchestra,
Where roaming, screeching seagulls squawk like roaring, moaning
clarinets,
And bashing, banging waves beat like drumming, beating drums.

An abandoned, bashed ship is tossed about like a clanging,
smashing cymbal,
While the rattling ship's horn blows for help like a screeching,
groaning flute,
Meanwhile terrified people yell on the sandy seashore like a beating,
banging piano.

Beneath the dark blue sea a jumping prancing sea horse swims
frantically like clanging, bashing maracas,
A small baby swordfish is biting like a happy, playful triangle.

Beware of the stinging, spiky jellyfish bopping about like a noisy
chanter,
As a group of dolphins swim merrily like a beating, bursting organ
as they play the melody of happiness.

The orchestra of the sea moves on.

Luke Campbell (10)
Kelty Primary School, Kelty

The Sea Is Like An Orchestra

The sea is like an orchestra where the sea crashes into the hard
stone rocks
Like angry loud cymbals
And seals shout and call, angry like a trombone.

Seagulls whoosh about like an energetic violin
And pebbles rub shakingly and squeaky like maracas.

The wind whistles like a droning, tiring French horn
And the sand falls delicately like a gentle triangle.

Wet rocks plop when water touches like a funky guiro
And trees rustle calmingly like a wind chime.

Under the deep blue sea fish swim like xylophones
And echoes move like fluttering acoustic guitars.

Sharks growl viciously like banging electric guitars
And seaweed waves like a sleepy harp.

The sea is like an orchestra
And makes me want to relax.

Mitchell Wood (10)
Kelty Primary School, Kelty

The Orchestra Of The Sea

The sea is like an orchestra
Where seabirds scream like whining trumpets
And waves beat like droning drums

Loud squealing seabirds like a screeching violin
And grass on the steep cliff rustles like gentle triangles
The hollow wind blows like hollow violins

And ships rattle like castanets clicking
The sea is like an orchestra.

Abbey Healy (10)
Kelty Primary School, Kelty

The Orchestra Of The Sea

The beautiful breath-stealing sea is like an instrument in a beach
orchestra,
Where screeching annoying seagulls scream
Like irritating high-pitched flutes,
And crashing heart-stopping waves beat like mighty thundering
drums.

A jet-black stumbling ship is tossed about like cymbals,
While the loud ship's horn blows for help like a deep moaning
saxophone,
Meanwhile screaming furious people like a rain stick scattering on
the beach.

Beneath the sea a vicious killer whale is hunting for survival
Like an out of tune piano,
While a dolphin is bobbing up and down like a smooth bass guitar.

Beware of the snapping crabs that will snap your toes like snappy
castanets,
Meanwhile a school of octopuses are playing the music of death.

Robbie Winsborough (10)
Kelty Primary School, Kelty

The Orchestra Of The Sea

The beautiful sparkling sea is like an amazing magnificent orchestra,
Where squawking, screeching seagulls scream like loud, moaning flutes
And thrashing, crashing waves beat like banging, booming drums.

A big, huge ship is being tossed around like bashing, clanging cymbals
While the sailing ship's horn blows for help like a thundering trumpet,
Whilst frightened people squeal on the wet seashore
Like a clarinet in a mighty thunderstorm.

Beneath the sea, a giant, evil shark hunts its prey,
Roaring like a huge bass drum.
Lovely, elegant dolphins glide in the waves like soft relaxing harps.
A small, colourful sea horse dances like twinkling Indian bells.

Beware of the orange, pinching crab,
Its pincers nipping like grabbing castanets,
A family of stingrays sting like screaming clarinets,
Zooming through the water.

Leanne McArthur (10)
Kelty Primary School, Kelty

The Orchestra Of The Sea

The beautiful blue sea is like an instrumental beach orchestra,
Where loud, noisy seagulls scream like gigantic squeaky flutes
And noisy, roaring waves beat like banging trumpet drums.

A big creaking wave is tossed about like a cool, great guitar,
The ship's horn blows for help like a loud, annoying trumpet.
Meanwhile small, petrified people on the shore sprint away like a
beating, thinking piano.

Beneath the sea there is a big, fierce shark hunting for fish to eat,
It's like a beat of a drum drumming.

Beautiful shining dolphins jump out of the water,
It's like a smooth twinkling triangle.
A small golden sea horse dancing, going round like circles,
It's like a big smooth trumpet.

Beware of the jellyfish with its stinging tentacles
Swimming through the water.
A group of sharks hunting for fish for their dinner.

Emma McMillan (10)
Kelty Primary School, Kelty

The Orchestra Of The Sea

The sea is like an orchestra
Where seashells rattle together like clicking maracas
And seagulls sing like broken trumpets.

The seals beat on the rocks like loud drums
And the dolphins like the same note on a piano.

The pebbles roll down the rocks like a rain stick
And the sand does a soft crunch under your feet.

The sea is like an orchestra
And it makes me want to relax.

Connor Syme (10)
Kelty Primary School, Kelty

The Orchestra Of The Sea

The prancing, dancing sea is like a magical orchestra
Where loud, stealing seagulls squawk like high screeching flutes
And hard smashing waves beat like crashing drums.

A petrified jet-black ship is tossed about like bashing cymbals
While the rattling ship's horn blows for help like a noisy, thumping trumpet
Meanwhile frightened people yell for help like a group of screaming dolphins.

Beneath the deep blue sea a terrifying, frightful shark
Hunts for fish like a thumping boomwhacker
While a crazy, snapping crab flees across the ocean like clapping castanets.

Beware of the horrible, hideous jellyfish that sting like a roaring vibrating electric guitar

As a school of octopuses surround their prey,
Playing the music of death.

Georgia Richardson (10)
Kelty Primary School, Kelty

The Orchestra Of The Sea

The sea is like an orchestra where sand rustles like weird maracas
And pebbles crash together like banging drums.

Seagulls screech like noisy violins,
Waves hit off the rocks like calm rain sticks.

Birds sing like clicking castanets
And seals lie around like loud trombones.

The wind whistles like a graceful trumpet
And the grass blows like a tickling xylophone.

Under the deep blue sea spider crabs walk like a guitar with a broken string
And sharks growl like vicious electric guitars.

Fish flutter like tinging triangles,
Whirlpools spin like weird guitars.

The sea is like an orchestra of the sea,
It makes me relax.

Lewis Wright (10)
Kelty Primary School, Kelty

The Orchestra Of The Sea

The sparkling blue sea is like a wonderful musical orchestra,
Where loud squawking seagulls scream like high-pitched flutes,
And huge flowing waves beat like hard booming drums.

An abandoned colossal ship is tossed around like a ragdoll,
While the destroyed ship's horn blows for help like a thundering trumpet,
Meanwhile startled families yell for help like a loud bass guitar.

Beneath the sea an elegant dawdling dolphin glides
Like a small quiet ringing bell in a church,
While small bobbing sea horses look for food like a loud golden trumpet.

Beware of the hermit crabs nipping and punching at your feet
Like brightly coloured maracas,
A big sharp pufferfish swims past like a small but loud horn.

This is the orchestra of the sea!

Sarah Marsh (10)
Kelty Primary School, Kelty

The Orchestra Of The Sea

The beautiful shining sea is like a breathtaking orchestra,
Where loud mouth seagulls squeaking hard play flutes,
And giant, smashing waves beat like booming thunder drums.

A petrified enormous ship is tossed about like a pelting, smashing
snare drum,
While the thumping ship's horn blows for help like a loud, beating
guitar,
Meanwhile frightened people shout for help like a screaming thunder
xylophone.

Beneath the sea a calm, glamorous turtle glides through the ocean
like a slow motion violin,
A fairly strong swordfish hunting for fish like a hard dramatic organ.

Beware of the frightening, powerful crab walking about on the
surface ready to pinch like clicking, clapping castanets,
As a school of dolphins come and play the music of happiness.

Brendan Lawrie (10)
Kelty Primary School, Kelty

The Orchestra Of The Sea

The beautiful deep sea is like a beautiful breathtaking orchestra,
Where screaming, squawking seagulls screech like a very loud flute
And gigantic crashing waves explode like loud smashing cymbals.

An enormous brand new cruise ship is being tossed like drums
getting played on.
The high-pitched horn blows for help like a very big trumpet.
Meanwhile people are terrified,
Trying to find shelter like a bass guitar.

Beneath the blue sea a diver,
A large frightful shark chasing its prey like a strong booming drum.
A beautiful smooth dolphin jumping like a slow relaxing song of a
violin.

Beware of the enormous strong whale
Like a terrifying piece of music played by an electric guitar
And a massive cruel octopus plays the music of death.

Lewis Taylor (10)
Kelty Primary School, Kelty

The Orchestra Of The Sea

The sea is like an orchestra
Where birds sing gorgeously like clicky castanets
And seals flop about like deep trombones.

Pebbles bang like angry drums
And the sound of sand crunches like noisy maracas.

Seagulls fly elegantly like a calm violin
And waves crash on rocks like trickling rain sticks.

Under the deep blue sea bloodthirsty sharks
Swim like a vicious electric guitar
And echoes spread like a fluttery acoustic guitar.

Long seaweed sways like a purring harp
And spider crabs pinch like a pinging triangle.

The sea is like an orchestra
And it makes me want to relax.

Louise Andrew (10)
Kelty Primary School, Kelty

The Orchestra Of The Sea

The sea is like an orchestra
Where the tide comes in calmly like gentle maracas
And the seals sing depressingly like a sad trombone.

The plops of water are dropping
And clicking like intensive castanets
And the sand shakes firmly like hard rain sticks.

Waves smash and crash heavily like loud cymbals
And seagulls do their high-pitched squawk like squeaky violins.

Under the deep blue sea graceful smoothing rays sound like calm flutes
And the spider crab pinches effortlessly
And does it like the soft triangle.

The sea is like an orchestra
And it makes me want to write about it.

Bethany Reekie (10)
Kelty Primary School, Kelty

The Orchestra Of The Sea

The sea is like an orchestra where waves crash like cheery maracas
And pebbles rattle like droning drums.

The seagulls of the seaside scream
Sounding like lovely violins
And the birds squeak like noisy castanets.

The sound of sand crunches like cheery maracas
And seals squawk like a sleepy trombone.

Under the deep blue sea where sharks growl
Like vicious electric guitars
And the seaweed sways like a purring harp.

The sea is like an orchestra.

Callum Fotheringham (11)
Kelty Primary School, Kelty

The Orchestra Of The Sea

The sea is like an orchestra
Where waves crash like cymbals droning
And pebbles knock like thudding drums.

The sound of sand crunches like rustling maracas.
Clicking sounds like castanets whining like birds.

Attractive seagulls sound like squeaking violins,
The grass on the steep cliff rustles like a fluttery flute.

Underneath the deep blue sea seals squeak
Like screeching fast guitars
And fish flutter like flapping xylophones.

Echoes move around like a fluttery acoustic guitar.

The sea is like an orchestra
And it makes me want to sing and dance.

Chloe Adams (11)
Kelty Primary School, Kelty

The Orchestra Of The Sea

The beautiful blue sea is like a noisy ear-ringing orchestra,
Where loud screeching seagulls scream like a high playing flute
And huge crashing waves beat like solid bashing drums.

A massive cruise ship is being tossed about like a cymbal crashing
While a warning ship's horn is blowing for help
Like a loud high-pitched trumpet,
Meanwhile terrified people are shouting for help.

Beneath the sea a wild vicious shark squeals like a booming drum,
A calm, beautiful dolphin's jumping in the air like a well-tuned violin.

Beware of the big dangerous killer whale
Like a booming, roaring boomwhacker.
A school of jellyfish plays the music of fear.

Zac McQueen (10)
Kelty Primary School, Kelty

The Orchestra Of The Sea

The sea is like an orchestra where rocks smash like the beat of drums
And waves crash like cymbals.

The birds cheep like clicking castanets
And sand rustles gently like maracas.

The seagulls flop like high-pitched violins
And wind howls like the hollow French horn.

Under the deep blue sea flopping fish flutter like tinkling xylophones
And whirlpools spin like guitars.

The sharks groan like electric guitars viciously
And echo more like an acoustic guitar.

The sea is like an orchestra
And it makes me want to relax.

Adam Alexander (11)
Kelty Primary School, Kelty

The Orchestra Of The Sea

The smashing cold sea is like a mighty breathtaking orchestra . . .
Where gigantic loud seagulls scream like soft, gentle flutes,
And crashing, roaring waves beat like banging, thumping drums.

A huge croaky ship's horn blows for help like an annoying big trumpet,
Whilst the ship was being tossed around like a soft playing trumpet.

Beneath the crushing shining blue sea
A vicious huge whale glides like a sparkling blue sea
Like a trumpet playing hardly.

Beware of the black squirting jellyfish flying like a slow stringy guitar
While the dolphins are gliding through the deep dark sea like a glimmering soft piano.

Amber Wallace (10)
Kelty Primary School, Kelty

The Orchestra Of The Sea

The big blue sea is like a big pool
Like the amazing orchestra
Where the crazy seagulls shout like a loud flute
And huge crashing waves beat like gigantic drums.

A scary, huge, crashing ship smashes like a tiny bottle
While the scared people on the shore scream like a trumpet.

Beneath the sea a jellyfish so squashy
Sounds like a magic cymbal
As a bad mean, horrible shark hunts for food
It eats like a beating piano.

Beware of the angry stingray that hurts things like a big rain stick
A whale so heavy swimming in beautiful sea
Like a big bass drum.

James Sullivan (10)
Kelty Primary School, Kelty

The Orchestra Of The Sea

The sea is like an orchestra
Where waves crash like noisy rain sticks
And the sound of sand sinks quietly like nice maracas.

The pebbles knock together like loud drums
And seagulls shriek like noisy violins.

The seals are slouchy like a loud and lazy trombone
And birds squeak, flopping like scary castanets.

Under the deep blue sea there is long green seaweed
Like a silent flute
And sharks growl like electric guitars.

Echoes move like fluttery acoustic guitars
And a spider crab pinches and sweetly tings.

Aaron MacDonald (11)
Kelty Primary School, Kelty

The Orchestra Of The Sea

The beautiful blue sea is like a sprinkling rain stick.
The white screeching seagulls are like a fast-played flute.
The bashing, smashing waves beat like stomping drums.

A smashed giant ship is like a trashed bass drum
While the squeaky rattling ship's horn blows for help like a scraped
banging set of cymbals.
Meanwhile scared terrified people call for help like booming cymbals.

Beneath the dark blue sea a fearless scary shark hunts for fish
Like a smashed bass drum.
A smooth gleaming dolphin splashes through the ocean
Like a dropped pair of maracas.

Beware of the fast fresh swordfish that swims the water like a fast
violin.

Greg Ireland (10)
Kelty Primary School, Kelty

The Orchestra Of The Sea

The sea is like an orchestra
Where the waves crash on the rocks like a rain stick
And sand crunches noisily like maracas.

The pebbles crash like the banging drums
And seagulls irritatingly squeak like violins.

The birds tapping as they scream like a trombone.

Under the deep blue sea
Flopping fish flutter like tingling xylophones
And whirlpools spin like guiros.

The sea is like an orchestra
And it makes me want to boogie.

Liam Wilson (11)
Kelty Primary School, Kelty

73

The Orchestra Of The Sea

The sea is like an orchestra where waves crash like soothing rain sticks
And sand crunches like shaking maracas.

Pebbles crack like loud drums
And seagulls squawk like a screeching violin.

Birds land like tapping castanets
And seals flop like a hugely loud trombone.

Under the deep blue sea dolphins swim, squeaking like violins
And seaweed sways like a purring harp.

The sea is like an orchestra
And it makes me want to play.

David Gray (10)
Kelty Primary School, Kelty

Rescue Me!

R escue me
E verywhere I go there's no one
S harks are watching me
C alls for help but no one hears
U nseen by everyone
E very time I call for help

M any memories of friends
E veryone missing me.

Christopher Watkins (11)
Kymin View Primary School, Monmouth

Rescue Me!

R attling shells clash against rocks that surround me.
E very sound that drifts around me reminds me of home.
S urviving . . . very little chance.
C ollecting bottles to send back out to sea, in hope . . . of a survivor.
U nder pressure, waves smash against sand dunes and rocks.
E ager to get off the island and see my family and friends.

M emories one by one shatter against the grimy rocks of the beach.
E nd of my . . . life.

Katherine Louise French (11)
Kymin View Primary School, Monmouth

Rescue Me!

R oaring waves lapping over me.
E verywhere rubbish floating around.
S urf crashes against the bleached rocks.
C *rash, clank* over the rocks.
U nder the sand, crabs creeping out.
E vening comes, still no one there.

M oving crabs coming closer . . . closer.
E ndless days ahead, of loneliness and fear.

Molly Kellaway-Hardy (11)
Kymin View Primary School, Monmouth

Rescue Me

R ippling waves crash against the rocks.
E verywhere I go . . . no one or anything to be seen.
S hipwrecked boats all over the island . . . but no sign of life.
C oconuts scattered along the sand, the only thing I can drink.
U ndulating dunes, ripple in the distance.
E very day goes slowly by.

M emories of home play in my mind.
E ndless days ahead, death or life. I don't know which one.

Liam Mills (10)
Kymin View Primary School, Monmouth

Rescue Me

R oaring waves clashing over the shore
E agles circling me for their food
S eagulls skimming the skies
C oconuts fall from their trees
U nusual fruits I've never seen
E verywhere I go places are abandoned

M y family . . . I miss them
E verywhere people have abandoned me. I'm alone.

Jack Moore (11)
Kymin View Primary School, Monmouth

Rescue Me!

R oaring waves coming towards the shore.
E verywhere around me is just sea and coconut trees.
S hipwrecked pieces floating around the rocks.
C hests of gold under the sand.
U ndulating dunes ripple in the distance.
E verywhere I look there is no help around.

M emories of home surround me.
E ndless days ahead, of loneliness and fear.

Mollie Brown (10)
Kymin View Primary School, Monmouth

Rescue Me!

R oaring waves lap onto the shore,
E verywhere there are coconut trees hovering over me,
S eeing the island deserted . . . scary,
C rab shells scattered along the sand,
U seless sticks lying around,
E agle-eyed . . . I search for help!

M emories of home dance in my saddened mind,
E ndless days ahead, of loneliness and fear.

Chloé Harwood (10)
Kymin View Primary School, Monmouth

Rescue Me!

R oaring waves lap onto the shore
E very day I search for a ship or person . . .
S eashells scattered all over the beach
C oconuts falling from the great tall palm trees
U nder the sand crabs make holes
E verywhere on this island is deserted

M emories of home don't leave my head
E ndless days drag by . . .

Lauren Jones (11)
Kymin View Primary School, Monmouth

Rescue Me!

R oaring waves crash against the rocks that surround me,
E verywhere memories of families,
S hipwrecks scattered across the shore,
C oconut trees . . . are my only hope,
U nder all the sand I finally find a bottle,
E verywhere is wood from the ships . . .

M y hopes are in despair,
E agle-eyed I search for rescue.

Saskia Ryan (11)
Kymin View Primary School, Monmouth

Rescue Me!

R oaring waves lap onto the shore
E verywhere is quiet . . . apart from the waves crashing
S hipwrecked against the ragged rocks
C oconuts ripening
U nder the shore, treasure lies
E ager to get off the island

M issing my family
E ndless days, rescue me!

Taylor Williams (10)
Kymin View Primary School, Monmouth

Rescue Me!

R oaring waves lap onto the shore.
E verywhere abandoned . . . the quietness surrounding me.
S urf crashes against sun-bleached boulders.
C one-like shells.
U nused bottles to write back home.
E verything gone . . . I'm on my own.

M emories clash in my head like the waves against pebbles.
E very time I see a boat . . . I cry for help!

Samantha Gittings (11)
Kymin View Primary School, Monmouth

Happiness

Happiness is like a blue balloon happy in the air
It smells like hot chocolate with marshmallows
It tastes like sweet strawberries
It sounds like joyful giggling
It reminds me of winning my first match
It feels like playing football with your mates.

Euan Williams (11)
Liberton Primary School, Edinburgh

Wonder

Wonder is gold like an artificial sun being launched into the sky to help scientists.
Wonder smells like the presence of the summit of Mount Everest within arms reach.
Wonder tastes like you are the first person to tuck into a newly released food that has now vanished mysteriously.
Wonder sounds like a bustling crowd just waiting to test out a new spaceship.
Wonder looks like the Leaning Tower of Pisa, almost about to collapse!
Wonder reminds me of the time we went to Transgression Skate Park.

Shreenil Vani (10)
Liberton Primary School, Edinburgh

Silence

Silence is white like a piece of paper
Silence smells like a misty, black, disgusting smoke
Silence sounds like when you're the only one in a graveyard
surrounded by old cobwebbed gravestones
Silence looks like stillness standing in the ruins
where your own home has just been blown up
Silence feels like a cold knife touching your neck
just about to give you a big gigantic cut
that stays there for your entire life
Silence reminds you of when you're alone in an old, ancient
little church all by yourself.

Chloe Lee (10)
Liberton Primary School, Edinburgh

Fun

Fun is yellow like the sun on a beautiful Sunday morning
Smells of lavender fields on a lovely day
Sounds like happiness and laughter while the sun is gleaming on the
fresh Scottish loch
Tastes of sweet cherries
Looks like everyone doing collaborative group work
Feels like people enjoying materials for art
Fun reminds me of my childhood.

Callum Donaldson & Lewis MacDonald (10)
Liberton Primary School, Edinburgh

Joy

Foamy pink marshmallows warming your heart
Achievement like getting in the cross-country team
Cheering with an extra hint of enthusiasm
Having bundles of fun with your friends
Butterflies fluttering in your stomach, sending a nice shiver up your
spine
Christmas, the excitement of opening all your presents.

Zoe Kitson & Cameron Tranter (10)
Liberton Primary School, Edinburgh

Silence

Silence is white like plain wallpaper ripped
It smells of nature dying, the wind howling through dark old trees
Silence sounds like people sleeping but dead
Silence tastes like no salt in the creeping sea
Silence looks like God who never created Earth
Silence reminds you of drowning, no one to save you
And your life slowly fades away.

Shannon Chan (10)
Liberton Primary School, Edinburgh

Terror

Terror is the colour of blackness in which I am stuck forever
Terror is the smell of sweat dripping down my forehead
Terror sounds like the screaming and the shouting
Along with gunshots ringing in my head
Terror feels like I'm dying in my cold grey coffin in the ground
Terror looks like blood everywhere, which I once saw
Terror reminds me of my life.

Ammarah Javaid (10)
Liberton Primary School, Edinburgh

Joy

It is the colour yellow like the sun shining on you when you score a
goal.
It smells like fresh air when you play tig in the park.
It sounds like Old Trafford cheering when Manchester United score.
It tastes like chocolate melting in your mouth.
It looks like Suso Santana scoring against Hibs.
It reminds me of my favourite football teams winning.

Robbie Urquhart & Denis McCance (10)
Liberton Primary School, Edinburgh

Courage

Courage is the colour of blue and yellow
Courage smells of happiness and relief
Courage sounds like birds in the air
Courage looks like the pure blue sky
Courage feels like joy everywhere
Courage tastes like sweet oranges and apples
Courage reminds me of the sun shining on me.

Damon Hutson-Boyle (10)
Liberton Primary School, Edinburgh

Love

Love is red like a ruby shining in the light
Love smells of jasmine in a cerulean bottle
Love sounds like the birds singing in the trees
Love feels like you're soaring above the angry world
But only you remain happy
Love looks like a blossom tree swaying in the wind
Love reminds me of all the good things in life.

Whitney Travers (10)
Liberton Primary School, Edinburgh

Fun

Gold like the sun shining down on me
Freshly cut grass in the meadow
Children laughing in the park
Kids playing with their friends
Exciting like when you're playing in the garden
Fun reminds me of the happiest moments of my life.

Emily Edmunds & Alexander Hamilton (10)
Liberton Primary School, Edinburgh

Relief

Relief is red, like your team scoring a last minute goal
Relief is like you have finally got that hot dog you always wanted
Relief sounds like a cheer when you are out of the traffic jam!
Relief feels like you scoring a goal for your team
Relief looks like Robbie saving a penalty
Relief reminds me of Hearts winning a game.

Ross Jardine (10)
Liberton Primary School, Edinburgh

Happiness

Yellow like the golden sun beating down on you
Smells like your favourite food floating in the air
Sounds like children cheering as your team scores a goal
Feels like when you score your first goal
Looks like children having fun
Reminds me of opening my presents on my birthday or Christmas.

Hannah Barclay (10)
Liberton Primary School, Edinburgh

Joy

Joy tastes like smooth white chocolate melting in my mouth
Joy sounds like Hearts' fans cheering at Tynecastle when Hearts score
Joy looks like my room filled with sweets and chocolates at Easter
Joy reminds me of when I went to M&D's with my cousins Andrew and Duncan.

Adam Cuff (10)
Liberton Primary School, Edinburgh

Fear

Black like you're lost in complete darkness
The smoke of gunfire swirling in the air
An ear-splitting scream that haunts you and will never leave you
A knife pointing at your heart just about to stab you
A hand grabbing at your throat, trying to strangle you
When my house was set on fire.

Naomi Shek & Iliana Ortiz (10)
Liberton Primary School, Edinburgh

Happiness

Happiness is yellow like a sandy beach on a hot day.
Happiness smells like fresh air on a sunny morning.
Happiness sounds like bluebirds singing to their little ones.
Happiness looks like kids laughing and running in the playground.
Happiness reminds you of your family having a hug.

Jade Chan (10)
Liberton Primary School, Edinburgh

What Is Black?

Black is a dog,
A Labrador too.
Black is a cat,
A witch's one, ooh!
Black is a feeling
Which is not a nice one.
Black is a car,
One that might go far.
Black is a crow
That nests in Granny's tree.
Black is a bucket
For bringing in coal.
Black is a cooker
That people cook on.
Black is a kettle
For making a cup of tea.
Black is a colour
But not for me!

Sarah Mackey (8)
Lisnagelvin Primary School, Londonderry

Happiness

Happiness starts with a great big smile
And knowing me, I smile for a while.
Happiness smells of yellow daffodils
And sounds like angels singing in the air.
It tastes like melting chocolate dancing on your tongue,
When you feel happiness you know fun has begun.

Leah Rosborough (9)
Lisnagelvin Primary School, Londonderry

Joy

Joy is yellow
It smells of trees
It sounds like the birds singing
It looks like a dog
It feels like the sun
It reminds me of having fun.

Latisha Magee (7)
Lisnagelvin Primary School, Londonderry

Happiness

Happiness is all bright colours, especially red.
It smells of roses, violets and apples.
It sounds like the ocean, the wind and the rainforest.
It tastes like cherries and berries.
It looks like a golden trophy, and the golden sun.
It feels like a warm breeze in bed.

Bradley Charters (10)
Lisnagelvin Primary School, Londonderry

School (Happiness)

I wake up this morning with a smile upon my face
Because today is sports day and I'm running in a race
I know I may not win it, I'll do the best I can
Then my gran will say, 'Great wee man.'

Kyle Lynch (10)
Lisnagelvin Primary School, Londonderry

Don't

Don't pet the dog,
Don't get lost in the fog.
Don't sink the boat,
Don't forget your coat.
Don't run out on the road,
Or you'll end up like the toad
Who forgot his Highway Code.
Don't hit the foal,
Don't dig a hole.

Caolan Cassidy (10)
Lough Road Learning Centre, Lurgan

Don't

Don't pet the dog
Do sit up
Don't ask for help all the time
Do go to bed early
Don't climb trees
Do keep away from bees.

Matthew Holland (9)
Lough Road Learning Centre, Lurgan

Love

Love is red, like beautiful red lips.
Love smells like strawberries, a nice smell.
Love sounds like birds singing through my ears with all of their songs.
Love tastes like sweet cherries from my mouth with a sweet taste.
Love looks like a beautiful sunset on a nice hill.
Love feels soft and cuddly, like a bear with all the hearts.
Love reminds me of a beautiful day with my friends.

Kelsey Henderson (10)
Lynburn Primary School, Dunfermline

Anger

Anger is black, like the sky in the whistling night.
Anger smells of smoke out of a firing chimney.
Anger sounds silent, like the shadow in the moonlight.
Anger tastes of blood running down my mouth.
Anger looks like someone in your family dying right in front of you.
Anger feels like a flaming hot bullet shot through your heart.
Anger reminds you of having a feeling that you are going to faint
And never wake up.

Erin Bathe (10)
Lynburn Primary School, Dunfermline

Wonder!

Wonder is wondering what is going to happen in the future.
Wonder is a bright orange in the sunlight.
Wonder smells like daffodils in the park.
Wonder sounds like the rain bouncing on the pavement.
Wonder tastes like sour yoghurt in your mouth.
Wonder looks like a dark, rainy sky.
Wonder feels like jaggy nettles jagging your spine.
Wonder reminds me of the dark, thundery sky.

Kyle Millar (10)
Lynburn Primary School, Dunfermline

Wonder

Wonder is the colours of a bright summer's day.
Wonder is the smell of everything sweet and nature so silent.
Wonder is the taste of freshly-cut rhubarb and sugar.
Wonder is the sound of birds tweeting
And the autumn is whispering through my blonde hair.
Wonder is when I look at the beautiful bright flowers
Freshly sprouting from the earth below my feet.
Wonder reminds me of newborn life, when I look at it, I wonder.

Shannon Devaney (10)
Lynburn Primary School, Dunfermline

Anger

Anger is the colour of red blood
Anger smells of smoke coming from a fire
Anger sounds like loud gunshots
Anger tastes like disgusting rotten eggs
Anger looks like being chased by a raging bull
Anger feels like being surrounded
Anger reminds me of people annoying me.

Aaron Brown (10)
Lynburn Primary School, Dunfermline

Anger

Anger is black like volcanic ash floating from the sky.
Anger smells like rubber burning in a house.
Anger sounds like an explosion bursting through the sky.
Anger feels like chocolate melting in your mouth.
Anger looks like fire bursting in the air.
Anger feels like you're on fire.
Anger reminds me of lava bursting from a volcano.

Daniyaal Uqab (11)
Lynburn Primary School, Dunfermline

Love

Love is red as a rose growing in the garden.
It smells like a sugary peach ready to eat.
It sounds like a cat purring.
Love tastes like melted chocolate and cream.
It looks like a newborn baby.
It feels like a puppy's fur.
It reminds me of a cuddle from my mummy.

Courtney Halkett (11)
Lynburn Primary School, Dunfermline

Silence

Silence is as white as freezing cold ice cream.
It smells like a dusty old lobby.
Silence is as silent as a cold, dark night.
It tastes like musty water swirling around in your mouth.
Silence looks like an empty room with nothing in sight.
It feels like jumping into a big pool of cream.
Silence reminds me of ghosts on dark, silent nights.

Katie Scott (10)
Lynburn Primary School, Dunfermline

Volcano

Mountain,
Quiet,
Countryside,
Peaceful,
Safe.

Volcano,
Boom!
Explode,
Erupt,
Eject.

Volcano,
Rock,
Ash,
Lava,
Flame.

Volcano,
Danger,
Disaster,
Destruction,
Death.

Jessica Martin (11)
Oakfield Primary School, Carrickfergus

Volcanoes

Volcanoes shoot out
Ash and rock.
When I hear this,
It gives me a shock.

When volcanoes explode
Lava falls down.
When I hear this
It makes me frown.

Up the crater,
The lava goes.
It starts to shoot out,
Like a hose.

Down the mountain
The lava goes.
The villagers flee,
In rows and rows.

The molten lava
Is underground.
It shoots up,
All around.

Kurtis Hamilton (11)
Oakfield Primary School, Carrickfergus

Snow, Snow

Snow, snow
It's very nice
But please, please
Don't walk on the ice.

Snow, snow
My name is Dan
In the snow
I build a snowman.

Snow, snow
It falls at night
In the morning
I have a snowball fight.

Snow, snow
It blows a gale
In the snow
I make a snow angel.

Jordan Spence (11)
Oakfield Primary School, Carrickfergus

Volcanoes

Volcanoes are warm,
They make a big storm.
They blow up the ground
And make a big sound.

Molten stone,
It is blown
Out of the mountain top.
It turns to lava,
That is a palaver.
It makes the volcano go *pop!*

Leigh Collins (11)
Oakfield Primary School, Carrickfergus

Volcanoes

When a volcano
Blows its top
It shoots out ash
And molten rock.

When lava shoots out
Children cry
Then, *boom!*
Everyone dies.

Then slowly
The land recovers
And the survivors
Come out from
Under the covers.

Luke Baker (11)
Oakfield Primary School, Carrickfergus

Revenge For My Teacher

My teacher's called Mrs Black
She has three little children
Once she put them in a sack
To stop them misbehaving

I put a whoopee cushion
On the teacher's chair
And I put a lizard
In the teacher's hair

But before you go to do that
There's something I should've mentioned
The teacher wasn't stupid you know
And put me in detention.

Evie Bennett (9)
Oakfield Primary School, Carrickfergus

Volcanoes

Volcanoes are big,
Volcanoes are tall,
In the unexpected lava will fall!

If it erupts, run a mile,
Just take my advice,
Or you'll be gone a while!

If you don't die,
Just go away,
And if you go back, why?

Catherine Cochrane (10)
Oakfield Primary School, Carrickfergus

Footprints In The Snow

Footprints in the snow
Lots and lots I know
Lovely white snow
Snowflakes make up
Some snow.

Snowflakes falling from the sky
White, white, I know why
Cry, cry, why, oh why?
I don't know why.

Natasha Millar (11)
Oakfield Primary School, Carrickfergus

Volcano, Volcano

Volcano, volcano you are so big,
When you erupt you do a little jig.

Volcano, volcano you give me a shock,
When you start firing out your rock.

Volcano, volcano, inside is magma,
When it comes out it turns into lava.

Volcano, volcano your lava flows
Down through the countryside and starts to slow.

Peter Campbell (11)
Oakfield Primary School, Carrickfergus

Volcano, Volcano

Volcano, volcano
Let's all be a volcano
I grow and grow
Let's all grow
But when I need to go
You better do it too
Run as fast as you can
Because . . . *I'm . . . going . . . to . . . blow!*

Abbie Murray (11)
Oakfield Primary School, Carrickfergus

Snow

Snow is white
Snow is bright
Ice will give you such a fright
Jack Frost will give you frost bites
Snow is thick
Snow is thin
Sometimes you can get snowed in.

Kyle Martin (11)
Oakfield Primary School, Carrickfergus

Winter

In bed at night
I hear the freezing wind
Blowing through my window
It makes my curtains move
And I shiver
Outside I walk
On the snow carpet
Whilst frosty fingers
Touch my spine
And still I shiver.

A storm comes
Pitter-patter turns into
Plip-plop then
Bang, bang!
Hailstones hit me
Thunder jumps me
I turn and run
Back to my bedroom
And I shiver!

Holly Cuttiford (8)
Oakleigh House School, Swansea

The Listeners

'Is there anybody there?' whispered the assassin.
The roar of his Aston Martin's engine
Frightened a vulture from the turret,
Which swooped over the assassin's head.
He asked again, there was still no answer.
Confused, he listened for any movement,
But all he could hear was the echo of his own footsteps.

He knocked on the door,
'I know you're in here,' he said.
They heard the creak of the door opening,
'Argh!' A bat flew into him
And he fell onto the statue of a knight
And the silver plates rustled.
He got back up and climbed up the marble staircase,
But there was no one there
And then the listeners could hear
The wheels of the car spinning on the gravel
And he was gone!

Ben Christer (10)
Oakleigh House School, Swansea

Haiku Poem About India

India's special!
India's tectonic plate
Crashed into Asia!

High, lofty mountains
Climbed up into the blue sky
And Everest rose.

Heavy snow falls down
Onto the cold mountain tops
And it never melts.

Gushing rivers flow
Down the mountainous landscape
To the thirsty plains.

The mountains are cold
And Everest is freezing
But down south it's hot!

Matthew Lawrence (8)
Oakleigh House School, Swansea

Power Rangers Everywhere

There are Rangers on the sofa
And Rangers on the fireguard
There are Rangers in the bedroom
And Rangers on the table
There are Rangers in the cupboard
And Rangers out the window
There are Rangers in the kitchen
And no Rangers in the toy box!
Whenever Blake plays with his Power Rangers
There are Rangers everywhere.

Saffy McCrae (10)
Rockfield Primary School, Oban

The Wonders Of The Sea

What does mankind do to these animals?
Shark fins into shark fin soup,
Whales into lipstick,
Dolphins floating to the bottom of the ocean,
Turtles caught and not being freed.

Ever wondered how colourful the tropical reefs are?
Beautiful types of coral,
Shoals of little fish swimming by,
Colourful starfish sticking to the rocks,
Tiny fish peeping out their holes.

Deep, dark crevasses
Hiding living fossils,
Leading down to an abyss,
A strange animal kingdom,
Sharks lurking in the black waters.

The stormy waves raging across the ocean,
Huge tidal waves crashing against the rocks,
Tsunamis destroying everything in their path,
Making the waves come.

At the end of the day,
Everything turns to calm,
Everybody leaves for home,
The moon reflects in the ocean,
The world goes to sleep.

Beth Campbell (11)
Rockfield Primary School, Oban

Glimmering Moonlight

What is the sea?
The sea is a vast ocean
Full of treasure.
The water is blue,
Full of life and glimmers too.

Smell the fresh, salty water,
Sand between my toes.
Stones scattered around,
In the water and on the beach.
In the day it shines all around
And in the night it sparkles in moonlight.

Sails glide across the sea,
Boats behind, queuing up.
I hear someone has won, so I turn around,
They're shouting, 'I've won, I've won!'

Fish squirm round and round,
Up and down the ocean wide,
They swim non-stop every day
To find food to eat at night.

Now I see a sailing boat,
The shadows of this calm, summer's night.
They're sailing very slowly tonight,
Drifting off before midnight.

Rachel Campbell (11)
Rockfield Primary School, Oban

Dinner Time Rhyme

Can you tell, if you please,
Who is it likes mushy peas?
How about Louise?
Louise likes peas.
How about Lisa?
Lisa likes pizza.
How about Dale?
Dale likes kale.
How about Hannah?
Hannah likes banana.
How about Sam?
Sam likes jam.
How about Zoey?
Zoey likes ravioli.
How about Mandy?
Mandy likes candy.
How about Mum?
Mum likes gum.
How about Betty?
Betty likes spaghetti.
How about Fred?
Fred likes bread.
OK then, what about Lady de Pompadour?
She goes home for dinner!

James MacIntyre (10)
Rockfield Primary School, Oban

Dinnertime Rhyme

Can you tell me, if you please,
Who it is likes mushy peas?
Louise like peas.
How about Kelly?
Kelly likes jelly.
How about Greg?
Greg likes an egg.
How about Holly?
Holly likes lollies.
How about Kate?
Kate likes cake.
How about Fred?
Fred likes bread.
How about Sam?
Sam likes ham.
How about Reg?
Reg likes veg.
How about Tom?
Tom likes ham.
How about Vince?
Vince likes mince.

Ok then, what about Jenna Ray Campbell?
She goes home for dinner!

Hannah (11)
Rockfield Primary School, Oban

Football

Feet kicking
Legs aching
Heart beating
Back leaning
Legs running

Crowd singing
Ball bouncing
Whistle blowing
Commentators shouting

Players happy
Coaches shouting
Trophy lifted
Smiles all around.

Arran Campbell (10)
Rockfield Primary School, Oban

Football

Feet kicking
Heart beating
Back leaning
Legs hurting

Crowd singing
Whistle blowing
Ball bouncing
Commentators talking

Players happy
Fans happy
Trophy lifted
Smiles all round.

Fergus Lawson (10)
Rockfield Primary School, Oban

Motor Racing

Legs gripping
Arms ache
Head looking
Back hurting

Crowds cheering
Engines roaring
Heart pounding
Wheels skidding

Champs again
Home happy
Celebration tea
Winner, me!

Michael McInnes (10)
Rockfield Primary School, Oban

Food Everywhere

There's food on the table
And food on the floor.
There's food on the walls
And food on the door.
There's food on the curtains
And food on the stair.
Whenever Daddy's eating,
There's food everywhere.

Abbie McDermott (11)
Rockfield Primary School, Oban

Custard Everywhere

There's custard on the table
And custard on his nose
There's custard on the walls
And custard on his clothes
There's custard on the floor
And custard on the door
Whenever David eats his food
There's custard everywhere.

Fiona McLean (11)
Rockfield Primary School, Oban

Flour Everywhere

There's flour on the table
And flour on the floor.
There's flour on the worktop
And flour on the door.
There's flour on the stool
And flour on the chair.
Whenever Granny bakes a cake,
There's flour everywhere.

Ruari MacNiven (11)
Rockfield Primary School, Oban

Mum Washing Clothes

There are clothes on my stairs
And clothes on the lampshade
There are clothes in the basket
And clothes on the floor
There are clothes under my bed
And clothes on my door
Whenever Mum does the washing
There's dirty washing no more.

Brian Logan (11)
Rockfield Primary School, Oban

The River-Leaf

One day, as I watched the water flow
From source to mouth, I saw it go!
Then, I had a funny feeling,
As from my branch I started peeling!
Suddenly I began to fly and flee,
I cried, 'At last I'm free!'
I glided down slowly,
Into the river I fell,
I've left my friends behind,
Where this journey will end, I cannot yet tell.

Through the water, watch me go!
Look! Look!
I'm going with the flow!
The water twists and turns
And I am carried with it,
Faster and faster the river flows and I can't stop it!
The sea is approaching fast,
Splash! At last my journey has ended.

Erin McIvor (11)
St Columba's Primary School, Kilrea

107

In One Moment

One moment I'm in light,
The next in darkness,
Covered in thick brown dirt,
After long, dark months I've become a beautiful wonder.
Now I'm standing tall,
Tall and proud,
Observing the special grounds
All around me.
I see children running, playing games,
Beautiful surroundings for me to take in.
My great friends everywhere to be seen
And animals in the fields beside me.

I hear the laughter of children playing,
The school bell ringing,
The shouts from the teachers
And the choir singing.

I smell the awful fumes from cars
And food from the kitchen.
The herbs around me,
Tea from the staff room.

I feel the branches of the trees beside me,
The sharp, sweet breeze,
Flowing through my fingertips.

I taste the whiff of marvellous herbs,
The crisp, sweet breeze
The droplets of rain that spoil the fun,
Then the very next day the rays of sun.

Now that's my day over at school,
It's time for bed,
To rest for the night,
Excited by what I'll see tomorrow.

Mollie Maguire (10)
St Columba's Primary School, Kilrea

My Senses Adventure

As I swoop from above,
I see joy all around,
From the children having fun
To the branches of the trees blowing.
I see the beautiful plants
And I see the ducks skimming the waves.

When the children go away
I hear their footsteps striding by.
I hear the beauty of nature
As the wind blows through the trees,
I hear the swans guiding the young ones
As they embark on their journey through the lake.

As I glide through the sky,
I smell the freshness of nature,
I smell the beautiful bluebells beginning to bloom,
I smell the herbs and the roses as the scent releases itself,
I smell the horrible scent of smoke in the air, causing global warming.

When I swoop through the air, I spot
A lovely bird house, with seeds left out just for me!
I taste the feeling of gratefulness
For the kind soul that fed me.

I feel the wind flowing through the air,
I feel the wind hitting my face,
As I fly though the sky,
I feel so free, like a tiger running free in the jungle.

And, as I arrive back at my nest,
I see the children having fun,
I smell all the beautiful flowers
I hear the trees swaying,
I taste the seeds from the bird table,
I feel the wind blowing past,
I feel great, I feel safe.

Bronagh McNicholl (11)
St Columba's Primary School, Kilrea

The Lonely Tree

Every morning
I wake up
To the rustle of the wind
Coming in my direction.

The early sunshine
Shines down through my branches
And into my eyes,
I can see, even though I'm almost blinded.

I can hear all the words
That the children come out with,
Their voices are so loud,
But some are so quiet.

I can feel the thistles
Pricking me
And the nettles
Tickling me.

I can smell the soft grass
And the freshness of the air,
I can smell the cows
And they don't smell so pleasant.

I can taste the water
Travelling up my roots,
The water tastes so cold
And refreshing.

I see it is night,
I hear mice scampering,
I taste the cold air,
I smell the leaves,
But I'm still just a lonely tree!

Caitlin Convery (11)
St Columba's Primary School, Kilrea

Just A Lonely Stream

I'm just a lonely stream,
Nobody cares,
Nobody realises
That I exist.

I see the early morning dewdrops,
So crisp, so fine,
Just lying there,
Tender and still.

I hear the rowdy, rambling children,
It's like they're breaking free from their shackles,
Free from imprisonment,
Just taking in the moment.

I smell herbs and rose bushes,
Drifting past me
Into thin air,
Like I was never there.

I touch the soft breeze,
Gliding on the palm of my hand,
It's like having a whole world at my fingertips,
I feel invincible.

I taste the cold air,
Like oxygen being pumped into me,
The feeling of warmth and care,
But the pollution turns my stomach.

I want to be appreciated,
But to people I'm just there,
No reason, no meaning,
I'm just a lonely stream.

Daniel Dallat (10)
St Columba's Primary School, Kilrea

Senses Stream

As I flow by the school, I hear
The Primary One children talking
Shouting, screaming, playing
And running about.

As I flow by the school, I see
The Primary Fours running
Up and down the playground
Like young children do.

As I flow by the school, I smell
The waft of school dinners
And the lunches
That the children have to look forward to.

As I flow by the school, I taste
The leaves that fall off the trees onto me and
The broken branches that have rotted away
And fallen on top of me.

As I flow by the school, I touch
The riverbanks and the branches
And the leaves and the rubbish
The breeze and the rain falling on me.

As I flow by the school
My senses turn on
And the feeling of flowing
By the school is fantastic!

Tiernan McGill (11)
St Columba's Primary School, Kilrea

My Life Is Just All Around Me

As I skip through the fields,
I see all the action at St Columba's every day.
When footballs are kicked into my field carelessly
Mum gets quite worried.

Everyday, without fail, I hear the children shouting madly,
I hear the cows mooing and my friends baaing,
When the children go into class I hear the trees rustling, relieved,
Now it's peaceful, the children are inside again!

I see all the outside classrooms,
The peaceful river,
All the equipment for the children
And the lovely swans floating on Craig's Dam.

I smell the lovely herbs in the herb garden,
The lunches of the children when they eat outside,
I smell the fumes that are taking over our environment
And most of all the lovely breeze on my face.

I feel the soft grass below my feet,
The warmth of my mother's wool,
The snow, as cold as ice,
The leaves floating around my pasture.

I taste the rich grass,
The creamy milk from the farmer's bottle,
The sharp breeze in my mouth.
Oh what a peaceful place.

Daire McKenna (11)
St Columba's Primary School, Kilrea

Standing Still But Watching All Over

I am sitting still,
Watching all over,
My beautiful leaves are budding,
Have you figured I'm a tree?

I hear children coming out to play,
Shouting and screaming excitedly,
I hear the radio from a car
And the splashing of water.

I see boys and girls
Running and skipping merrily,
I'm watching cars passing by
And in a flash they are away.

I feel the boys and girls bashing my trunk,
Breaking my branches,
I also feel the gentle breeze
Brushing against me.

I taste the rain
Travelling up my trunk,
I taste the soil around my roots
And it tastes so toxic.

I smell the polluted air,
And the chip shop up the town,
Oh, it smells so pleasant
And the herbs in the Year 2 garden.

Conor Gillen (11)
St Columba's Primary School, Kilrea

I'm Just A Big, Old, Lonely Tree!

I'm just a big, old, lonely tree,
All I can hear is children shouting with pleasure,
I can hear robins chirp with glee,
I can hear the wind blow loudly,
I can hear the stream splish and splash,
I'm just a big, old, lonely tree.

I can smell the herbs which Year 2 planted,
I can smell the flowers in the garden,
I can smell the fumes from the cars,
I can smell the food being delivered,
I'm just a big, old, lonely tree.

I can see the cars rushing past me,
I can see foxes scurrying below me,
I can see horses galloping everywhere,
I can see butterflies fluttering over me,
I'm just a big, old, lonely tree.

I can touch my long twisted branches,
I can touch my new buds,
I can touch my green leaves,
I'm just a big, old, lonely tree.

I can taste the nutrients in my roots,
I can taste the freshness of my new leaves,
I can taste a brand new tree,
I'm just a big, old, brand new me!

Ciara McShane (11)
St Columba's Primary School, Kilrea

Going With The Flow

I am a weighty raindrop
High up in the sky
I feel the clouds getting heavier
It's time to say goodbye.

I am a showering raindrop
Soaking everyone below
Trying to make my way to a river
Where I can safely flow.

I am a lively raindrop
Swishing down the waterfall
Coming to the edge of it
I hear the sea call.

I am a mighty raindrop
Growing bigger as I go
Bending, twisting round the bends
The current swishes me to and fro.

I was a tiny raindrop
And with my friends we grow
We're now a beautiful river
And raindrops join our flow.

Eimear Hegarty (11)
St Columba's Primary School, Kilrea

Do You Know What I Am?

As I wake up in the morning,
I hear *broom, broom,*
The lorries warming up for the daily run,
The birds are singing in the sun,
The children are playing, having fun.

The day passes on and I'm quite peckish
So I take a lump of the juicy, green grass,
All alone on the wide open vast.

As I view the distant horizon,
I see a lonely deciduous tree
Standing out there, nowhere to be,
As if banished from its friends,
All alone, no foe or friends.

As I wander about, I smell a smell
Coming from the mill,
It is the lorries filling up for the daily thrill.

Night fell and the stars shone,
As I slept I dreamt that this day
Was an extraordinary day.

Shea McTaggart (11)
St Columba's Primary School, Kilrea

I'm The River . . .

I am the river,
Wide and strong, for me to travel it doesn't take long.
The raindrops pitter patter as they hit me strong,
But I shall still flow along.

I am a river,
Nice and bright,
I glow through the night,
I'm a very pretty sight.

I am a river,
Peaceful and fast,
I've passed many tasks,
Hills and fields and to the ocean at last.

I am a river,
Sometimes clean,
But when I'm polluted I'm not a pretty scene,
So everyone, be nice and green.

Paddy Quigg (11)
St Columba's Primary School, Kilrea

I'm A Strong, Long River

I'm a river, fast and wide,
I can be short and I can be long.
I float through the night and rush through the day,
You can be sure I'm always strong.

I am a river, unique in many ways,
I can be cold and I can be hot.
I can be rough and I can be calm,
One thing's for sure, I change a lot.

When I get dirty my fish die,
When I stay clear and clean my wildlife thrives.
I'm important, humans need me to survive,
So if you drink me, you're sure to stay alive.

I am played in by people
And some take my fish.
They take me for granted, showing no respect
And tease me by eating their catch from a glowing dish.

Jack O'Connell (11)
St Columba's Primary School, Kilrea

Down At The River

River the long, river the great,
Looks like it never goes to sleep.
I can see the angelic swans seeking for food,
The radiant fish with joy by my light.

When the clouds are away and all rise up in the sky,
I make it evaporate, so it won't get too deep.
But when I'm away and the clouds float up high,
It gets very deep when the raindrops aren't asleep.

People enjoying a picnic, listening to the flow,
Enjoying my sunshine rays.
Children splashing and swimming in the river,
Diving and chasing the scared little fish.

Now the winter's coming, snow everywhere,
Animals running to their little homes.
During the cold, dark days the fish will be gone,
Now, until spring, I will be alone.

Roksana Malinowska (11)
St Columba's Primary School, Kilrea

Fluffy Sheep

I'm running around the field
With my brothers and sisters.
I hear my mum shout, *'Baa, baa.'*
She wants me to go over to her.

Mum wants me to get food,
I take a lick of a meal,
Then I push and fight
With my brothers and sisters for milk.

I lie down and it is very quiet,
I can hear children playing football
As I lie down in the soft grass.
The sun comes out,
We get up and play together.

Niall McFerran (11)
St Columba's Primary School, Kilrea

Love

Love is different colours, but mostly red,
Like a pair of my mum's shiny, red high-heels.
Love feels like someone kissing you on your cheek.
Love sounds like romantic songs floating in the air.
Love tastes like candyfloss at the fair.
Love moves with the clouds everywhere.
It smells like a field of roses around you.
Love is like romance and it's in everybody's heart.
But my dog, Firen, is my favourite love.

Laura Lesniak (9)
St Malachy's Primary School, Newry

Happiness

Happiness is the colour of yellow daffodils.
It smells like the lilies I get for my mum.
It tastes like sweet, soft, fluffy candyfloss.
It sounds like children playing and having fun.
It feels like my stuffed teddy when I hug it.
It moves like a gentle breeze on a scorching hot day.
It lives in my heart nearly all the time.
It is a lovely feeling.

Glenn Murray (9)
St Malachy's Primary School, Newry

Love

Love is red like roses.
It smells like a garden of carnations.
It tastes like strawberries and fresh cream.
It looks like a rainbow on a sunny day.
It feels like my mummy giving me a hug.
It sounds like my friend's dog barking at me.
It moves like time and it never stops.
It lives in my house every day.

Caroline Shields (9)
St Malachy's Primary School, Newry

Love

It smells like roses in the garden.
It sounds like music you play while you dance.
It tastes like strawberries and cream.
If feels like a hug you get from your mum.
It lives at home with me and my family.
It comes from deep inside your heart.

Jamie Lee Anderson (9)
St Malachy's Primary School, Newry

Love

Love is red, like roses
It is the sweet smell of a field of bluebells
It tastes like hot chocolate with marshmallows
It sounds like birds singing in the morning
It feels like my dog Bobby licking my hand
It moves like the water in my fish tank
It lives in my heart and people I love.

Cíara Níamh Maginness (8)
St Malachy's Primary School, Newry

Anger

Anger is the colour red, like blood.
It sounds like thunder rumbling during a storm.
It tastes like hot chilli sauce.
It feels like a balloon bursting.
It smells like smoke from a boiling volcano.
It moves like a rocket in space.
Anger is Hell!

Niall Jennings (8)
St Malachy's Primary School, Newry

Love

Love is red.
It smells like roses in the summer.
It tastes like a mint sweet on your tongue.
It feels like a ride on a pony for the first time.
It sounds like the waves in the sea creeping up the beach.
It looks like a golden summer sunset.
It lives inside my heart.

Caitlin Ward (8)
St Malachy's Primary School, Newry

Anger

Anger is like a red, blazing fire.
It smells like black smoke from a volcano.
It tastes like a spicy pepperoni pizza.
It sounds like a hurricane hitting a house.
It feels like a rough, scaly dragon.
It moves like a cheetah pursuing its prey.
Anger is like a tornado.

Anthony McVeigh (9)
St Malachy's Primary School, Newry

Happiness

Happiness is all the colours in the rainbow.
It smells like roses in the air.
It tastes like a delicious Malteser cheesecake.
It sounds like children laughing on a summer's day.
It feels like a warm, cosy bed on a rainy night.
It moves like a roller coaster with the wind blowing on my face.
It is in my heart most of the time.

Padraig McDonnell (9)
St Malachy's Primary School, Newry

Happiness

Happiness is the colour purple.
Happiness is the smell of freshly mown grass.
Happiness is the taste of vanilla ice cream melting in the sun.
Happiness sounds like my mum's voice when I awake.
Happiness feels like the fluffy fur of my dog, Susie.
Happiness moves through the air.
Happiness lives in my heart and I hope it will always be there.

Sandra O'Hare (9)
St Malachy's Primary School, Newry

Love

Love is bright red.
It smells like a garden of lilies.
It is the delicious taste of Cadbury's chocolate.
It sounds like the wind blowing through your hair.
It feels like your mummy hugging you when you go to school.
It moves quietly, like a cat creeping up on a bird.
It lives in your heart every day.

Alannah White (8)
St Malachy's Primary School, Newry

Anger

Anger is red like a blazing volcano.
It smells like a fire burning.
It tastes like blood going down my throat.
It sounds like a meteorite hitting a building.
It moves like a spaceship in space.
Anger lives in Hell.

Evan McClurg (8)
St Malachy's Primary School, Newry

Polar Bear

P owerful jaws, strong teeth
O bviously scary if you come face to face
L ively and bouncy, catching its prey
A fright if you pass it on a dark night
R oars so loud it will deafen you

B ecoming endangered very soon
E very second of your life
A n ice patch melts before your eyes
R eally white, like snow.

Madeleine Chelmis (9)
St Nicholas CW Primary School, Cardiff

125

World War II

Planes hovering overhead
Children crying
People dying
Another four families dead!

Boom, boom! Bang, bang!
All you hear is guns firing from the sky
Then all the people die!

The annoying siren wails out a bellowing sound
Adults scurrying
Bombs emerging
Terrified people galloping around

Boom, boom! Bang, bang!
All you hear is guns firing from the sky
Then all the people die!

Planes firing them down as rapid as a stream
Barrage balloons defending
Children evacuating
Is this real? It seems like a horrendous dream!

Boom, boom! Bang, bang!
All you hear is guns firing from the sky
Then all the people die!

People moving to the countryside
Terrifying war
Bombs dropping no more
Safe in the beautiful countryside.

Boom, boom! Bang, bang!
All you hear is guns firing from the sky
Then all the people die!

Ieuan Lllewellyn, Weiming Ma & Niall Routledge
St Nicholas CW Primary School, Cardiff

World War II Brownie Explosion

Ingredients:
10 exploding bombs
1 jar full of the black smoke hovering over London
1 gallon of the German pilot's cold and slimy blood
6 spoonfuls of the crumbled bricks from innocent people's houses
10 tons of corrugated tin from the Anderson shelters
22 handfuls of shrapnel left over from the dangerous bombs

Method:
Firstly drop half of the exploding bombs into the cauldron, like the Germans dropped them onto London.
Throw 1 gallon of the German pilot's cold and slimy blood in, so it makes a thunderous *splash!*
Now plonk the rest of the exploding bombs into the bubbling mixture, so that it should burst into roaring flames, then settle back down within one minute.
Simultaneously pour in the jar of black smoke and the 10 tons of the corrugated tin from the Anderson shelters and hopefully a giant ash cloud will rain down over the mixture.
Launch in all the 22 handfuls of the sharp shrapnel and then the monstrous ash cloud will decrease down slowly and relax.
Then release the 6 spoonfuls of the crumbled bricks from the innocent people's house.
(Warning - release it with only 1 hand, otherwise the mixture will collapse like the crumbled house in the East End of London).
When the sparkles explode out of the mixture, that's when it's ready to explode in your mouth and tickle your taste buds.
If every British soldier eats this, then Britain will win World War II!

Jasmine Stevens, Mia Sexton & Olivia Donaldson
St Nicholas CW Primary School, Cardiff

Animals

C himpanzees
H umans are related
I t is great to have them around
M y home is being destroyed
P lease help
A re endangered
N ever let me die
Z ooming across from tree to tree
E veryone loves them
E ven me

S wing now chimpanzee
I love you
M ake us happy
I will be there
A ll of the time

T ry to survive
R un away
O ff you go
G o and play
L ost forever
O ff they go
D ying out
Y ou can help
T o save them all
E verlasting cuteness
S ave the chimpanzees!

Zac Messner (9)
St Nicholas CW Primary School, Cardiff

Giant Panda

G iant pandas are very cuddly
I ll they can be if we don't help
A ll kinds of pandas are in danger
N ever will they live if we don't help
T here are only 1,000 pandas left

P andas are too cute to be true
A ll baby pandas are the size of a mouse
N ever die pandas, because we will help
D anger! Danger! They're dying out
A lways will be loved

Bethan Ash (9)
St Nicholas CW Primary School, Cardiff

Gorilla Gorilla

G orilla, gorilla, that's me.
O ther than eating we play hide-and-seek.
R unning and running up and down.
I live to eat bananas.
L icking fleas off each other.
L ying in the sun.
A nimal in danger.

Jennifer Thomas (9)
St Nicholas CW Primary School, Cardiff

Panda, Panda

P andas, pandas
A re endangered
N ever see them
D ip and hide behind leaves
A sk us all for our help.

Ellie Inker (8)
St Nicholas CW Primary School, Cardiff

Rattlesnake

Watch me rattle by.
I live in the hot desert.
People take my rattle.

Mason Parsons (8)
St Nicholas CW Primary School, Cardiff

My Dog, Max

Max, what more can I say?
He acts like a furry Vax!
But his big, bushy tail
Is the opposite of frail.

As I come down with his food,
I can see he's in a good mood,
Wagging and ragging from side to side,
But when he's naughty he goes off to hide!

Oh boy! You would be amazed at the things he breaks
When his huge, chocolate brown body shakes
And my gosh, my grace, you would not believe the things he ate!
But give him a chilli, that's what he would hate!

But at Easter he spotted *my Crème Egg!*
And with puppy-dog eyes he did beg and beg and beg!
When I woke up in the morning, guess what was gone?
My Crème Egg! Like someone had stolen it with a tong!

I love my dog,
Even though he acts like a hungry hog!
I guess we never will know what happened
That Easter, when my *Crème Egg was devoured!*

Ameerah Mai (11)
Ysgol Cae Top, Bangor

Busy Bee

I am always under your tree
when you see me you will
shout . . . 'A . . . bee!'

I am at work every day to
collect pollen, to make honey
honey is sweet, I like it
on toast, it is so nice
it is never gross
I am just a bee
please don't kill me
if you stand on us and me
there will be no honey
all the flowers will die
goodbye.

Angharad Bronwen Roberts (11)
Ysgol Cae Top, Bangor

Help Me

'Help! Help! I'm drowning,
The water's pouring over me,
I'm sinking, help me.'

'I'm coming - I'm coming,
Don't worry, I'm coming.'

'Pull me - pull me,
I'm really sinking,
Please, please, help me,
Yay, yay! I'm free!
Thank you, thank you
For helping me.'

Rahil Ralis (10)
Ysgol Cae Top, Bangor

October

O ak trees growing
C louds are thinning
T he leaves are crunchy under your feet
O pen the door and let me in!
B unnies jumping around, feeding on carrots
E ating candy
R ed candlelight in orange pumpkins.

Tashi Bennett (11)
Ysgol Cae Top, Bangor

The Lad From York

There once was a lad from York
Whose favourite food was pork.
He had a smile
That would stretch for a mile,
But my, that lad could talk.

Bryn Berkeley (11)
Ysgol Cae Top, Bangor

Yorky, Porky, Forky

There was an old man from York
Who ate cream with a fork,
He went on the ground
And all he found
Was a boring piece of old pork.

Carla Edwards (11)
Ysgol Cae Top, Bangor

Dream

One day I looked outside my window
And I thought I saw a monster,
But I was having a dream,
Cos I was woken from my dream,
I must be mean.

Joel Rooijakkers (11)
Ysgol Cae Top, Bangor

My Pet, Jerry

My favourite pet is Jerry,
If he was a girl I'd call her Nelly.
He lies there all day,
Dreaming away,
Thinking, *what will I do today?*

Amy Goater (10)
Ysgol Cae Top, Bangor

The Moon In The Light

I woke up one morning and looked outside,
It was a surprising sight,
The moon was out, but it was light!
I wonder if it will be there tonight?

Esme Jones (11)
Ysgol Cae Top, Bangor

Young Writers Information

We hope you have enjoyed reading this book - and that you will continue to enjoy it in the coming years.

If you like reading and writing poetry drop us a line, or give us a call, and we'll send you a free information pack.

Alternatively if you would like to order further copies of this book or any of our other titles, then please give us a call or log onto our website at **www.youngwriters.co.uk**.

A platform for your poetry!

Young Writers Information
Remus House
Coltsfoot Drive
Peterborough
PE2 9JX
(01733) 890066

Get in touch!